An Alien Life

Colm Hannon

First Published in 2010 by TAF Publishing

ISBN: 978-1-907522-18-5
A CIP Catalogue record for this book is available from
the British Library

Typesetting and cover design and photo by Oscar Duggan

Published with the assistance of The Author's Friend.
For information about Assisted Publishing, including
catalogue and titles, visit www.TheAuthorsFriend.com

Printed and bound in Ireland by Gemini International Ltd

An Alien Life

Copyright © Colm Hannon 2010

Dedication/Acknowledgments

So - who me? My life has been a mix of all-sorts. From a backward wee gasúr, to a fairly tough boss. From a reluctant learner, to a writer with a strut. From a survivor of the old days, to a stranger in the new. I'm so happy with my wife and family. So grateful for the amount of help I've got along the way with my writing. Such support and advice is a must. I thank you all.

How To Record A Life?

How to record my life? That is my quandary.

To put into words all the happenings, accidents, incidents, calamities, collaborations, successes, failures, and wonderful memories of someone who has lived over seventy years on this never-still orb called Earth.

To record accurately what the World was at, at such a time; and how it affected our 'hero'.

When you collect marine animals there are certain flat worms so delicate that they are almost impossible to capture whole, for they break and tatter under the touch. You must let them ooze and crawl of their own will onto a knife blade, and then lift them gently into a jar of water.

Perhaps that might be the way to write this book?

To open the page and to let the stories crawl in? For I ain't no goddamn word-smith. I ain't fitted with a brain that can call up the right words at will, and set them down like they were set there by some Steinbeck or Miller.

But I'll do my best - sure what else can I do?

It all starts in 1938 - October 30th 1938, to be exact.

It is a significant date for two reasons: our 'hero' was born on that night; and a certain gentleman called Orson Welles chose the same date to broadcast live, a programme on American radio called *The War of the Worlds*. He announced to the listening public that we were being invaded by Aliens. I could never really forgive that large and talented genius for such an act. But, alien or not, I'd landed!

While there is no doubt that some of my behaviour may be alien to a lot of people, and even serve to alienate a lot of people at different times, I think the tale will verify my own belief that I am wholly innocent of all, or most, accoutrements of guilt.

Enough of all that. I will now hand you over to the man himself - me.

After all who knows the story better than me?

Before the War I arrived. Aye, before Adolf and the boys started their marching across other peoples' lands, causing well told harm and destruction. Doesn't it seem a long time ago?

So here I am now in the 21st Century, attempting to recall in some detail, my world and all that has happened in it.

Enjoy.

Colm.

Darting Fro and To

I've seen the grey stones of Wicklow.
Met a Bray head-the-ball.
Had a walkey in Dalkey.
Threw a black rock at them all.

Called to a don called Leary.
Pointed out a good sea point.
While of bridge of balls is best avoided,
A row at Westland could anoint.

There may be an odd still organ
In the confines of the south side.
Might even be prayers at breakfast,
Prior to a Leopardstown ride.

You can buy fine mutton in Sutton,
The best this town can sell.
Get a boat to Howth to celebrate
Before they ring that bell.

Pearse can be fierce at sun up;
Connolly a holy show.
But when my horse loses yet again
I could kill Lester with a blow.

The Harmonstown harlot's a terror,
Puts Baldoyle's biddies in the shade.
But when Donaghmede donna showed a need
I thought I had it made.

There may be a port called Marnock.
Even a tool to mal your hide.
Balbrigadoon may call the tune,
But Skerries stands upside

Escape

It's Friday; Friday is good.
I can suspend normality today.
Maybe for the whole weekend.
Today I can smile - for a while.

You see, I get paid today
so I can behave normally.
I can buy things, meet my
friends; even buy my round.

My little boy he's funny, he is.
Last Friday he came with me.
Later he asked me: 'Does everyone
get paid in a post office?'

Camara Da Lobos

Five palms bedeck the promenade.
Tall, imperious, proud.
Five locals view the passing scene -
Bi-vocal, parochial, loud.

Opposite, huge cliffs rise from the sea.
Granite-faced, impenetrable, styled.
The islands molten history visible
In natures timeless display.

Nearby a church bell tolls.
Each quarter measured, and hung out.
Occasional voices sing out their hymnal sound
Enriching the cacophony of Lobos in tune.

The side-streets and the chatter fill our smiles,
As we once again find favour with this town.
I struggle for the words to smuggle home,
To capture for all time the Madeiran charm.

One last look at the singing hills around,
With dotted roofs of local orange tiles.
The tunnels through the granite mountains say:
All is possible, and all is smiles.

One last taste too, of local wine.
Our one-armed bandit scurries to our side.
It seemed the toll had risen in our wake, but
In Heaven one does not question the price.

City Boy

To me, it is my life;
it surrounds me. With
all it's slipshod ways,
it is still ol' Dublin.

Oh, I've seen it
change. Progress -
if it is progress?
From then until now.

Then, it was passive -
welcoming. How it
welcomed this brash
kid, and bade me stay.

How can I not long
for the things that
memory holds dear?
The things of yesteryear?

I liked to see the
horse pull its dray
through streets and lanes, laden
with the goods we craved.

What need for 18-wheeled trucks?
With their choking presence?
No need then.
Perhaps - no need now?

Colourful hats, high heels,
and nylons for the ladies day.
With gowns and hair-styles
For the evening's trawl.

Bicycles bore many to their
destinations. Two-wheeled
independence with no
petrol, no tax, and no hurry.

Horatio oversaw all then
before he, too, took leave
of us. Though in a more
ignominious way.

I stroll this city now,
aware of the fume-filled
air. Aware of how much I
too have been left behind.

Sometimes I can still
feel its heartbeat. When
I am receptive to it's
suffering, it speaks to me.

Dervla

Travailing the
side-tracks of the world
right into old age;
she shames us lazies.

'Wheels within wheels,' spoke
loud the wandering soul.
The ever-onward, seeking,
informing mind.

Her written words bring
knowledge of far-flung
lands. Her delightful
sure style empowers

Her readers, giving us insights
into alien cultures. May I say:
'Thank you. stravaigler of antique
lands, and more miles to you.'

The Colour of Hope

The mood is veering off-colour.
My grey hair matches the skies.
The wife wonders if I've noticed
the red wine matches my eyes?

The colour-less woes of winter
leave me very little scope.
So I put all my aspirations in
the hands of that blue word called Hope.

1965 was when England called.

The destination of the desperate, you might say.

Maybe - I know that when the thought first entered my mind, I discarded it. Not a serious option, I thought. But then, I'd tried Dublin. Loved it of course, but it wasn't exactly alive and flourishing job-wise in those days.

Why didn't I go to College? Okay it was an option, no denying that. It was what any 'bright' boy or girl would do, given the chance. But I wasn't that bright. Book learning just wasn't the kind of thing I could handle. I'd had enough of that. I felt my brain needed some different direction. I was good with my hands - useful. I could fix things. I could get satisfaction from working with my hands. So, with the right stimulation, I thought I'd find the right choice.

'Leave this country. Get away. Get new experiences - escape.' That's what that little voice was telling me. To be honest, I didn't fancy the idea. I liked my own country. I liked the way of life. I liked the craic. But craic wasn't getting me anywhere. I was on my own and in desperate need of support - guidance even. Neither was available. Sure, some would talk of options - usually with the same old story, 'go to college'. I mean, I scraped through the Leaving Cert. I worked hard at it, and still got a very poor result. It just wasn't my thing. I even felt, while going through the 'learning' process: Why am I doing this? Do I care what Cicero said to one of his cronies a few thousand years ago? Do I really care if x plus y equals z - given the right circumstances? And who exactly am I going to be talking Gaelic to, when I leave?

Okay - anyone should have a modicum of knowledge to get them through the daily routine - but all that nonsense they forced us to learn? I've no memory of anyone sitting down and talking of the practical things of life to us. No talk of what we'd be facing when shunted out of those halls of learning. Nearly everything that did manage to root itself in my limited brain during those years was happily discarded on walking out those school gates. Yes, I know a certain amount of geography; I can add up numbers in my head with no trouble; I have a smithereen of history, and an appreciation of both English and Irish; - but I had most of that when I left National School.

Another five years of gathering mostly useless information didn't seem to me to make any sense at all - so why not England?

Getting on the old boat that morning was the loneliest moment I ever experienced. As it pulled away from the shore, and I could see my country being left behind, I felt a desolation that no man should have to feel. There was an intense aloneness embedded in my mind; a feeling that things surely can't get any worse. The looks on the faces of the other passengers did little to alleviate my woe. Mostly I guess, we were in the same boat - if you'll excuse the pun. There was a necessity inherent in all our leaving. Some, because of the need to earn money for themselves and for the family left behind. Some because of how their lives were 'over there' now, and through an accumulation of circumstances - could not be otherwise. "It's a hard ould road." said one gentleman to me, as he looked into the far distance and seeing nothing but hopelessness. That look has stayed with me through the years. Indeed, I have seen it replicated many many times as I met - in the bog-holes of England - so many of the displaced-dispossessed-and the desperate.

Arriving in a new country brings many feelings to the fore. If on holiday, the excitement and looking forward is topmost. If visiting somebody, then they, and their well-being, will take priority over the new surroundings. But, if going to find work and to make a new life for yourself, then there are going to be many mixed emotions churning away in your mind. While there might be a grudging appreciation of the new land, (at least you were being given the chance of a fresh start), I think the over-riding feeling is one of rejection. Rejection by your own country, for a start, and rejection by the 'system'. Maybe sometimes too, by your family? But man is a tough creation, mostly anyway, and adjusts quickly to a brave new world.

For myself, I didn't feel too bad about it, not once I got used to the idea anyway. Incredibly, I still didn't know what I wanted to do with my life. I was determined though, to take a little time and find a niche where I would be happy to spend my working life. I was fortunate to have a sister to go to, for a little while anyway, while 'adjusting' as you might say. So Liverpool was my first destination. I settled in with my sister, her husband and family, and did some reconnoitring.

Liverpool wouldn't be my first choice to live in - not then, anyway. I was certainly made very welcome in my new (temporary) home, but the contrast to what I had been used to was just too much. It was a rough and ready city, then. I found the scouser English to be a strange mixture of gruffness and politeness, of arrogance and good manners; and of inquisitiveness and pre-conceived opinions. Maybe they were confused by my refusal to fit into any of their ready-made 'boxes'? The secret to 'managing' them, I found, was to treat them as equals. That ensures that their initial off-handedness leads to a respect for you, and from then on you have the upper hand. They are not as smart as the Irish, in my extensive-experience anyway. Not as sharp, and certainly not as cool. But while visiting London, which I did a lot of over the following few years, I often had the opportunity to have conversations with the older generation who always fascinated me. Maybe I wondered how such a race, going by those I'd already met, could possibly have had such an enormous affect on the wider world - for good and bad over the centuries? Well I have to admit that they provided the answer. Most impressive and most genuine - everything that the younger generations weren't. My experiences of the latter over the following years, only confirmed this opinion.

Liverpool wasn't all bad. It was after all, the home of the Beatles; and 'young' music was flourishing. In my memory, while Ireland - including Dublin - was still trying to come to terms with 'rock-and-roll' around '64 and '65, over there it had found an easy home. Change was in the air, and by God change was going to be welcomed.

Youth, possibly for the first time in history, had not only found a voice but a mighty loud voice at that - one that was going to wipe away the former oppression for good and always. I sure liked that. If there was ever a good time to go there, it was probably then. My one problem was that the few quid I had was quickly taking flight, and the need for a regular income was upper-most in my mind. I said goodbye to my most generous hosts, and headed south.

My next stop was Oxford. Why? Because in spite of being 'independently-minded', I was also 'no eejit'. I had an aunt there, plus her family. Not just an aunt though - the best aunt that anyone could possibly have. She was the kind to throw up a perfectly good pub in Sligo, and follow her husband over. He was the kind to retire from being a Sergeant and go to Oxford, walk into a building site and say he was a carpenter, and 'any chance of a start?' Well he must have been good at the job, because he got that job. He must have been good at manipulating timber 'cause he worked away at it for the next twenty years, at least.

A Wander

After attending and participating in a reading in the city of late, I decided to wander a bit afterwards. You can get into a pensive mood betimes after experiencing a form of creativity. It tends to slow you down, in a way, and set you off on a different tack. Thus was I. Ventured across the water and bravely entering the lair of the dreaded 'Southsider'. I passed by the gates of that imposing seat of possible learning overlooking Dame Street. Many's the dame that paraded in front of those gates since they first opened in their pernickety way. Across the road, I spy that tobacco shop where I used delight in their wondrous selection. What a pity we sometimes get 'sensible' and discard such consolations.

I throw a longing eye up Grafton Street with its pose and show. Maybe I'm remembering the chug of a spitting bus, or a flagging motor when they claimed their space there? Body turns left instead. Kilkenny Shop still delights. Though perhaps the mere admiring glance at a window isn't quite all that those inside would have wish for. High wall on the left seemed to tell me that: 'there are those that belong inside my portly portals -and those that do not.'

My slow step quickened. Dawson Street impresses. Those twin bookshops devour time; and impart the means to spend hours sensibly. Mansion house - quite a building. Ahead, that Green. When passing by in younger days, our eldest said in low dudgeon: 'Why isn't there one named after me?' Youngest indulged in a winning smile. It is indeed a wondrous place. That hotel, now refurbished, I was seldom inside. Yet I do have a full appreciation of such an established establishment. Private clubs hang around this street, catering for those who badly need the absence of 'ordinary people' when indulging.

Straight on leads to Baggot Street and beyond. A side street used to provide a home for one of our first night clubs - Zhivago's. Was it about '70 that I temporarily ran into she what was to become permanent? Or did she run into me? I fear such insight and knowledge is denied to the mere male. I know such a place was a shockin' welcome-release from the prevailing and pervasive world of show band and ballroom.

Offices now take over most of this square mile. Many's the sweaty hour and day I spent in such. Installing, fixing, selling and cursing - telephone systems and such. How easily we leave the past behind for good. I believe I enjoyed it all - at least at the time I believe I did.

The world of museum, gallery and such, take up a lot of space. The square's seem suitable, somehow - all magnificent in their splendour and contents. Surely we should all make time to regularly visit and appreciate all they house? Especially the National Gallery. The fact that our Dail is delicately placed in the same environs must be a testament to wit - could it have been transferred from some South American junta?

How elegant the houses that occupy the surrounding streets - bygone splendour, you could say. But how sad the wee minds that destroyed the Georgian magnificence; replaced with what was to become our future. Regression starts here, ha.

I reach the canal and seek a seat - in the midst of money, in the surrounds of hounds, in the bristle of bustle. I find a peace beckoning - this ol' town, I luv ya.

A City Odyssey

Come on, then Belinda, tell me what happened in the job.

I don't want to talk about that, thank you very much.

But you're my sister, and I care about you.

Well, if you care so much, then give up this incessant questioning.

But I mean - Guinness'? They're such a good company - shouldn't you have stayed on?

It's good for you, you know.

Oh Jack. I forgot you were there. What's good for you, Jack?

Guinness, of course.

Don't give him any encouragement Petula. And please change the subject.

OK, if you insist. But it's great to be home, so it is. Did you know I've been away nearly forty years? Dying to see the City again, so I am. And this train - what do ye call it? The Dart? How quaint. But isn't it great?

Yeah - if you say so, Petula. Anyway, nearly there.

And what are you going to do when you get there, Jack?

Oh, I thought I'd have a bit of a ramble. Ya know; for old time's sake, like. In honour of your homecoming Petula my love.

Stroll into the old Met maybe, and have a quick half.

Later, I might treat myself to a liquid lunch at the Metro.

I might just also climb the old Pillar one more time - in your honour, so to speak. Maybe you'd join me?

Well I, I; listen you. We'll do our own thing, and you do yours. Just make sure you're back here in time for the four thirty train, - and don't dare be late.

Ya boss. Certainly boss.

God Belinda, you're very hard on him so y'are. I mean look at him - walking off on his own, and looking so shattered like.

Jeez Petula. Will ya ever cop on? That fella'd buy and sell the two of us ten times over, and then get drunk on the proceeds, You've just been too long away, that's all.

Now - what do you want to do?

Oh, just wander, I suppose; get the feel of the place again, like, and hear the accents.

Ya know what I mean?

How about a cup of tea before we start then?

That'd be grand. You pick where we go.

Oh Bewleys? How lovely.

Tea, is it?

Cawfee would be nice.

You mean coffee? Yep, coming up.

It's just as I remember it. just great.

The prices are not so great.

And it's not even owned by Bewleys anymore. Ah - what a shame.

In the States you just can't get a place like this anymore, you know.

Now, Belinda; Jack is gone and there's just the two of us. So you've got to tell me about what happened.

I suppose I'll have to tell you sometime, though I'd prefer if people minded their own business. However; I was getting on famously in my job, and really liked it. Besides being a part-time secretary to one of the directors, I was also asked to escort visitors to the plant;

To show them around, and explain the brewing process - that sort of thing.

You? You were asked to explain all that ? I mean ... gosh.

And me only a woman, you mean?

No. I mean Yes. I mean ... I mean you don't even drink the stuff.

I shall ignore that rather stupid remark, and carry on.

One day I was in the process of showing a large consignment of rather small Japs around,

And they expressed a wish to see into the large vats.

As they were paying rather a considerable sum between them, I got permission and we made our way to the top.

All was going fine too, until one of the little beggars dropped his silly camera into the vat.

Well, there was pandemonium.

I, to my cost, tried to retrieve it. Then, with all the jostling, didn't they knock me in?

You what? You fell into the vat? Full of Guinness? You fell?

Kindly keep your voice down.

And kindly remove that silly grin from your face, thank you very much.

Sorry Belinda, but what happened next? Did you not sink?

Well, they managed to pull me out; and you can imagine the kerfuffle - and ceaseless babble from that drove of Japs.

But how did you feel?

What an extremely silly question, Petula. - you should have been a reporter.

How do you think I felt?

Besides being exceedingly wet, not to say humiliated; and it didn't help that they were all insisting on taking endless photos of me.

I could have happily thrown each one of them into that damn vat from whence I came.

Unluckily, the noise had alerted others, and soon the whole damn place knew about it.

Of course - I had to leave.

I see. My goodness.

And-tell me, did they easily accept your resignation? And did they behave, well, reasonably?

You mean - did they ask me to stay? And did I get a good pay-off?

The answers to those rather cheeky questions are: yes and no.

They asked me to stay, said that it would all blow over,

But no, I didn't get a particularly great deal.

I'm on only half my pension, if you must know, and therefore have to continue working - though only part-time.

So there we are. I've told you, and you're the only one who knows.

You will, of course, tell nobody - understood?

Yes of course.

Though, I mean, Jack is your husband, after all, and ...

Especially Jack - Okay?

Do you think he's alright?

On his own and all? I mean...

Don't start all that again, Petula.

Please; besides I think you'll find that we'll run into him somewhere before this day is out.

So, where to next? A gallery? A museum?

You know, now that I'm a tourist - that's what I should do.

Yes, what about the Hugh Lane gallery?

The Municipal?

Sure why not? A short walk.

Later. Well, what did you think?

I just loved it. So much to see; and free too.

Favourites?

Oh - Osborne. Absolutely.

And you?

I'm afraid I'm still a Yeats fan; never changed.

All those Sligo scenes, and the horses when you can find them.

Isn't he a bit abstract - or something?

Or something?

Anyway, what's next? More culture?

Ah well. why not wander slowly towards the National Museum?

Never been there either; can you believe that?

I must say Petula, that silly twang of yours does not suit you.

Oh come on now - near forty years? Ya gotta allow. It ain't that bad.

It isn't that good, but come on.

We'll cross the Ha'penny Bridge and be up there in no time.

So much seems different, though. Has a lot been knocked down - or am I imagining it?

A lot - for better or worse

Lady, this City is changing quicker than Beijing.

Oh my gawd!

Whatever's wrong Belinda?

Just look at what's coming down the road Jack. Aw gosh; isn't that great?

Come on, let's dodge in this doorway and we might miss him.

No way, Belinda - I wanna see him.

I shan't ask why.

By the way, Bel; you know how he said he was going to climb the pillar and all?

I mean it isn't still there, is it?

It's just that he caught me off guard for a moment, and...

For gawd's sake woman - aren't we just after walking down O'Connell Street?

Did you see it?

Ah, there yiz are - me two floozies.

Sure ye'ed never know who ye'es meet in this ould town?

My thoughts exactly and how are you, my lovely Petula? Always lovely to see your smiling face.

Still the old charmer, isn't he?

I hadn't noticed.

Maybe ye two ladies would accompany me for a drop o' the crater' - seeing as its lunchtime?

How kind of you to ask Jack.

Belinda?

I suppose so.

Then folly me - O'Neill's it is.

Haven't been there since I worked in the Corporation.

We used meet there on a Friday, after work.

Wasn't I the unlucky man not to meet you then? What wild times we'd 've had.

Ah, Jack. Weren't you twice as lucky to meet Belinda?

Are you getting us lunch, or staying making stupid chat all day?

Certainly I am. What are ye havin' then?

Such a selection. Never heard of most of them. Maybe I'll just have a cucumber sandwich, and a vodka and white.

Cucumber and vodka? Obviously a woman of immense taste. And you, Madame?

Just get me some soup and brown bread.

Ah'm ... .yes. Right away, Madam.

God, Belinda, you're ...

I know, - you said it already. Very hard on him?

Now excuse me for a moment, please.

Ah, there y'are, me lovely Petula.

Ahm - where is she?

Oh, she'll be back in a minute, Jack. Don't worry. Hope she doesn't hurry; gives us some time together.

Oh now - you trying to make her jealous?

Some chance.

But she's very jumpy these times. Didn't you notice?

Maybe it's her age, Jack? We're all getting on a bit -and her leaving that job 'n all.

What're you two talking about?

Your lovely sister was telling me about you leaving your job, that's all.

Oh? Was she now.

I tell ya one thing; you can't fall into a good job too easy nowadays.

What? What? What did he say? Fall into what?

It was just a remark Belinda, that's all.

I told ya - jumpy.

Isn't it strange though - all those young people having lunch in here? I mean, don't any of them bring a lunch-box to work with them anymore?

For gawd's sake woman, will ya grow up. That lot, with a lunch box?

And a flask of tea, maybe?

Some chance.

Ah, they have it aisy now, so they have.

Born the wrong time, so we were; the wrong time.

Ah now Jack, I'd say you had some fine times when you were young, too.

Golden moments in a lifetime, my dear. It's all we can ask for.

God Jack, you're a bit of a poet.

'Buddy, you wouldn't know it - but I'm a kinda poet.'

'One for my baby,' Jack? 'And one more for the road?'

What d'ya say?

A Life of Words

Sixteen. Nineteen sixteen.

I was ten then. I was thin then. Thin and smart. Thought I was smart.

Lived in Foxrock. Did things by the clock. Never seen a fox in Foxrock. Once saw a rock.

My Dad was a rock. A rock of sense. Gave me few pence. Worked hard; least I think he did. Spent a lot of time at work. Same thing?

My Mum was good. A good Mammy. A good Mummy?

They talked of war; they talked of sport too, but mostly 'the war'. Didn't like the sound of it. People being killed.

Then they changed tack - changed flack. It was closer, somehow. They talked of Dublin and the 'fighting'. I asked if they were talking of 'the War'? Got a belt on the ear. Or was it a flea in the ear? She didn't like it; he didn't fancy it. I asked could I go in and see 'the fighting'? No chance. No dance. No dancing then; I was only ten.

The wireless talked of 'the rising'. Confusing. Too many 'the's'. Felt out of it; but within a shout of it. At school they talked of nothing else. Teachers seemed to know; seemed to show. I kept asking what was going on? One teacher lost his rag; lost his bag. 'Feckit Beckett.' he shouted. Hated that. Feckit Beckett. They all called me that. For a time.

But I was smart. Won them over. Then in clover. Liked the books. All those words. Millions, maybe. Why did people only use some? I was going to use them all. One day. When I wasn't ten. Wasn't thin.

Teacher said I'd better pay attention now - or I'd never amount to anything. Maybe he was right. But I passed exams. All the time. 'Tests' they called them.

Enniskillen, too. Different. Different strokes up there. Tough.
Got good at sport, though.

'The Rising' came and went. So did our visitors. Hate it when
they stay too long. Ruins the friendship. I wasn't too bothered.
Either way. Every way. Seemed like fun.

Then people started fighting again. Which 'the' is it this time,
I wondered?

Dad said he didn't want to talk about it. I went out and
walked about it. People were sullen. Except Benny Cullen -
he was laughing. I asked him why? He said his uncle had told
him 'the Irish were daft as brushes. They finally gets rid of
their enemies and what do they do? Do they celebrate? Do they
heck- -they start killin' each other. Old tradition'' he said. Daft
as brushes.'

I joined Benny in the laughing. Said I'd like to meet his uncle.
'No one in my house made me laugh', I said.

I grew up. A bit. Moved on. Went to college. University they
called it.

Different stroke. Different sport. Tried cricket, even golf.
'Flog' I called it. New words. Consumed with words. Bigger
books now; bigger words. 'This is my game.' Ì smiled. My
game'. Teachers encouraged; now.

'The fighting' stopped now. Peace, they called it.

Relieved. Too much to be done. Too much to learn. Became
aware. Aware of my lack of awareness. I read. Then I read
more. So many books. More exams; more swotting. Moved
on.

Wanted me to teach. There. Reluctant. Reluctant teacher.
Itchy feet. Itchy mind. Felt tied down. Felt restricted.

What I wanted I didn't know. Didn't know. Had to move -
had to groove. New word. New world? Had to find it. Ireland?
My world? New world ... .somewhere.

J J moved. In touch. Interested. France? For me? New world.
Moved. Grooved. Left behind my world. Man now. No student

me. No more. Not me. Except - … student of world. New world. New chances. Moving easy. Moving body easy. Easy part.

Dublin can't move though. Ireland stays. That's problem, I thought. Nothing changes. Speeches don't change. Promises of future. 'Dev' ducks and dives. Jives? No jiving here. Not yet. Church annoys; Mulloy's?

Later, man. Later. Settle in. Buy pen. Now I'm grooving. New language. Love it. New world? Don't repeat. Who…me?

One day found myself smiling. Shocked. Who is this man, I wondered.? In danger, I thought. Danger of happiness overcoming. Don't allow. Too Dangerous. Too restricting. Not me. Gravitas. - Better word. Assumed Mantle. Ahhh..' I sighed.

Bought pencils … ..better than pens … more immediate - more paper…more notes-more books … more words. In element. In filament.? Get serious. Who …me? Start to be serious. Felt natural. Strange. Serious, writing. oh yes. Down to it. Up for it.

Ireland gone; Dublin a memory. Problem. Stayed. Effecting my thoughts; effecting process. Can't shift it. Still miffed at it. Use it. Use it up… Only way.

Books evolve. Unsolve. Plays. Plenty plays. Publish. Good feeling. Wait for talk; always talk. Will they like? Will they buy. Which is important? They like; I hide. They want to talk; want to squawk . I'm talked out. Nothing to say. It's all there. Read. Meanings? Don't ask. Confusing … who..me?

More plays ; more amaze.. More questions … no answers.

Get older. Older. Wiser? More adviser. Proust wiser. JJ too. better than me. Encourage each other. Miss my mother; and my brother. He's the fortunate one. Blessed with anonymity.

Miss my land? Sometimes. Write of it enough. Too much? What I do. Won big prize. Don't know why. Must like me - must take care of that. More confusion? Course. Will ensure I'm more popular when dead. Made for life, then.

The future? All behind me now. All worded out. Go on? Don't know. Hard to go on.

Loved my life? Loved my wife. Life ok. Grateful for words. All those words. My tools. Go on? - Until the death. The last 'the'. I'll go on.

A Straggler on the Loose ...

I trundle towards South Georges; and as far as Camden Street and so on. Straight on is Charlemount Bridge which leads to Ranelagh.

Before the bridge is a dog's home, run by a few vets. People bring in stray dogs; they treat them, medically, look after them for a while, and find new homes for them. An admirable business, I think; and it obviously must pay, though they don't charge for the dog, initially. I know all about it, as I got our one and only dog there, quite a while ago. So I've very fond memories of the place. Yes-I may well go back and pick another one - someday soon.

Again, to stroll along this canal is hard to resist. There is, somehow, a feeling of things not having changed that much, after all. The quiet waters have an effect on me that makes me want to slow down and reflect. I do so, before heading back towards Rathmines Bridge. And Portobello.

There is a familiarity about the place. From way back, yes, but still there. The familiarity would be of one arriving from afar, and seeking some abode hereabouts. It was a Mecca for such; maybe still is. Flats galore. Small shops - staying open for all hours, to catch that last stray, that had run out of tea - or tobacco. I used to visit a lot, then. There was an unspoken, shared world there; a shared anxiety, maybe; a shared feeling of helping each other find their feet. But always too, a feeling of optimism; of things moving forward and lives getting sorted. Students from third level with their instant knowledge and admirable optimism. Others, in their first job, and excited by the possibilities opening up before them.

Rathmines - gateway to the future. Portobello. Don't ya love the name?

Certainly 'The Lower Deck' has nice memories for me. It always had good music and great atmosphere, as I remember it. Once, too, I was in there with some young lady, and the 'MC' called out my name to come up and sing a song. Seemingly someone had sent up a request. I got some shock. I pretended I didn't exist, of course, in spite of the persistent calling. I couldn't see who had sent my name up, either.

Strangely, a few years later, down in Camden Street the same thing happened, and this time I did go up and in fact did so most Saturday nights. Isn't it amazing what torture people can take too?

The old Olympic ballroom was further down. I could never take to it to be honest. It was a bit too 'Irish' for me then. Coming from somewhere without the tradition of ceili's, or old time waltzes and such, I found it hard to adjust. Maybe I was a natural convert to rock n roll?

Mind you, having an in-built aversion to things 'Irish' was not something I felt proud of, either. Particularly the language. Ignorance is no excuse for non-appreciation.

I wander up Rathmines Road again. For old times' sake. Further on is Rathgar Road, and points south. More salubrious, and less inclined to take in the rabble into their valuable homes. The old Rathmines cinema, one of the last of the originals. Opposite, the road into Ranelagh. A likeable town that must indeed have been most desirable in the old days. If not still. What impressive houses they are.

Once, when we both met Johnny Bohan and his new wife in his local there, we had parked across the road. When going, I was pulling across the road when I was hit by an oncoming car. It just got my door and it flew open. I was thrown outwards and my left hand automatically went up, as I fell. My girlfriend, soon to be my wife, caught my hand and pulled me back, just as my head hit the pavement. While I got a severe cut on the forehead, there is no doubt at all that her quick action saved my life. Sure I had to marry her then. Also, that was the last time we saw Johnny Bohan.

In spite of all that, I always felt Ranelagh to be a 'homely' place. Beechwood Avenue has special memories.

Further on is Milltown, where I often went to see the Rovers play. When they still played there, that is.

Then Dundrum, and the mountains. Not for walking to, not now.

Retrace. Down Adelaide Road, and into Stephen's Green. What a place. Have never seen nicer. Once, when our two boys were much younger, we were driving by it, and we told them what it was called. The older boy said: 'Why isn't there one called after me?' Yes-the younger one was Stephen.

I dwell a while. A good while. It is like a therapy, I find, to do so in such a place. Indeed, the frantic world just outside the gates could have been far away. There is something about being on foot, though, when in the right frame of mind, that makes you feel superior to the poor motorist. You are more in control, somehow, and less hassled.

Exiting by the southern gate brings me eye to eye with the imposing Shelbourne. Should I go in? A treat, maybe, on a 'different' day. Hell no, not on my own. I'd feel more at home in a corner pub, with a sandwich, and a black pint. It's only right that people should know their place - don't you agree? I've a grudging admiration for the place, though. It seems to straddle the centuries, with style. Straddle the old and new Irelands, indeed.

Perhaps the 'Dawson', around the corner, would be more to my taste. Smallest pub in Dublin, they used say. I struggle for standing room. Listen to the various stories being relayed all around me. What fascinating lives some people live, eh? Such a place is a must for any eternally aspiring writer. I resist the urge to take out that note-book and pencil. I suppose, even with my sieve mind, enough might dally, to be rekindled some time, in the darker future. Makes me wonder how much is 'original' in anyone's writing, really.

I resist the urge to 'have another' and move on. The personal odyssey must continue, I feel.

Dawson Street. I suppose I think of the book shops first. Two admirable and venerable old ladies they are. Of course I must dally. How they eat up time. I struggle to leave, without a purchase; knowing there will be a return. To travel light, is to travel easier.

Back to more familiar territory again. Circles, eh? Not that that place called Trinity is familiar. Well- outside of it is. Oh, I've been to plays there; and a concert. Have even been shown around one of the labs. But that's it. Hell - I'm no bleedin' academic, anyway. Sows ear, and all that.

Down around Andrew Street, and such. Old work memories, mostly. Old telephone exchanges, and old post office. Years travelling around here, I was. Gas times, mostly. And the little Trinity bar - now re-named - where every row and argument had to be sorted out. One way or another.

Hayes, Barry, Redmond. Where are ye now? The night Telephonists would join us, usually. So you often wondered why you couldn't get a reply, when looking for a number? Silly Billy. Much more serious business to be sorted - in the Trinity.

Crown Alley exchange was across Dame Street - one of the oldest exchanges. Now it is surrounded by rather different clientele than then. It is part of Temple Bar, no less. That manufactured haven for the 'sheik' and affluent. Quite impressive buildings, I must admit, though. The 'Square' I just love. Night time springs a different scene, though, on the casual visitor. The serious business of carrying on-and on-the age long habit of imbibing gallons of strong liquor will be found to be in full swing, and into the late hours. Our neighbours like to come and join in, tasting proper beer for possibly the first time, and 'making a show of themselves' in the process. Our own, more used to the strength, perhaps, concentrate on getting as much into themselves as quickly as possible; later to splatter the surrounding footpaths with the resulting mix. Youth, you might say, showing that a certain affluence doesn't always bestow a certain dignity. Jealousy? Maybe-but I hope not?

But there are gems to be found here, too. Like the Irish Film Centre; worth a visit, even without going to see one. The Square on a Saturday is a must - if you like chocolates, home-made cakes, and lots of fat-making goodies. Not for you? - course not.

Dame Street; this meanders from the grandeur of College Street and its promises, to the more realistic environs of Thomas Street. It squirms by Dublin Castle, and its huge history. It is very much a traffic freeway, with cars upon cars, easing through, hour after hour. Again, the only way to move about is by foot.

Take a look at Parliament Street, on the way. It had a fine hotel, the Royal Exchange, where my folks used sojourn, on their occasional visits, in the 50's, and before. I do believe it once had the honour of housing me - about '48. It was probably the only time I had a bed to myself, up to then. It is sad, I think, that such a place as it is no more. This street, though, is the keeper of some abodes that sell beer from small private breweries, and is worth the visit - by the enthusiast. What an impressive sweep it is, though, from the bridge right up to the Castle gates. Can't you just see the carriage and four trotting its way, with its oh-so- important visitors?

Werberg Street - where that 'chip shop' resides. Stop for a treat? Of course.

Francis Street, a bit further on. Now we're getting to the real heart of things. Can't you just feel the heart-beat? The Coombe area all around. Used work down here, when Sound Systems had their ramshackle premises, just off the Coombe Road. So much development since then. So many of the old shops and houses gone, to be replaced by the new. There was a place further up the lane, then; where dead animals found their way; and whose smells used waft on the breeze, to greet and visit any passing nose. Memories - of all sorts, all around.

Pimlico, just a little further on, past the hospital. What a beautiful place it was, I always thought, with its small, perfect little houses. Like an enclosed community, almost. No doubt called after Pimlico in London? Or maybe the other way around. Didn't Ealing Studio once use it for a location in one of their great films? Good ol' Stan Holloway and such? Anyway, this one is not that changed, I'm glad to see.

Dolphins Barn further on, and Crumlin; with Rialto to the right, down the South Circular. But, I feel the weariness descending; ageing bones soon remind when enough miles are chalked up. I give in, and hop on a bus. Another day can see to the next stage on my journey through this city; and all its treasures. But I hop off again at Wexford Street, just to trundle through, once more, that last kilometre-or so- before the city.

Maybe I missed a memory or two? Let's see. That dip in the road before hitting Exchequer Street. On the left corner was a dentist's rooms, back in about the 70's. A gas place, alright. He was a real playboy. Liked to hire really good-lookin' women as receptionists; probably thought it would bring more custom. Where did he get that idea, I wonder? He didn't go in for making appointments, or such; just walk in. Once, I was in a fight near Christmas, and I got a front tooth broken. I rang him and he said: 'come on over - you can't go around looking like that for Christmas?' He fixed me up with a temporary tooth.

The Long Bar -still as I remember it. One of the good old stock. Many's the 'rendezvous' I had there. The Connacht Restaurant used sometimes supply a 'mate.' How'ya Julie, remember me? No? Good. There's that telephone exchange again. Just a look in the door - no more. Plessey boys all long gone now. Split to the four winds, I suppose. Jackie Hayes-from Cabra. There was a good pal. Big shock of red hair, and a personality to match. He used put bets on what colour the telephonists' knickers would be, as they climbed the steps. I don't think I can ever remember him not talking. I miss him, a lot. A select band, we were, traversing the exchanges of the city; and indeed of all the big towns, updating the equipment, and updating the local population on the vagaries of man. It all started for us right here in Exchequer Street.

Across the road was, and is, South William St. Not a lot there for the likes of us. The Civic Museum of course; but even they wouldn't take Hayes. I suppose it was a fairly small circle we all traversed in our lives, then. Work-pub-betting shop-pub-girl friend's flat-home-work-pub. Is it any different for any young fella - even now? Doubt it. Not a lot of time spent shopping, as I remember. The minimum amount. Some would be more particular, and try to co-ordinate colours, etc. The suit, though, would be looked after. A bit tatty, maybe; just a little worn; but shining. There was always someone one had to try to impress. Happy days, though. Moving on.

The Quays always supply me with food for thought. Don't really know why. The narrow side-walk always seems to be teaming with life. Maybe I just notice it more there. The anxious and weary faces at the bus-stops; the multi-coloured reality of our new -and varied -population. The obvious variation of cultures; children slung-seemingly precariously, sometimes - in a makey-up sling, across the front, or back. They seem quite content with their carriage; guess they've been in there since the beginning. Locals, on the other hand, push and pull, hassle and shout, and drive themselves to distraction, in the daily rumination of getting from A to B. Some come bearing bags, and wheelie cases; probably from

Heuston Station, returning-or on the first tentative trip-to a new life.

How different it must look to them, than it did to the likes of me, in '58. How different they are too, perhaps. They exude confidence. They'll do alright, I think to myself. How good it is to see a generation that are almost born with hope and drive. It is in the faces of the young I find consolation. And a certainty of progress.

Capel Street doesn't show much progress. Still that conglomeration of furniture shops; and crawling traffic. The odd little shop selling 'phones catches my eye; hard to rid the mind of a lifetime's occupation, I suppose. Barely recognise what are now the new generation of communication's paraphernalia. What wondrous things they all promise. I remember selling a system once that had 47 different 'facilities'. They never used more than five.

Interesting to see so many 'apartments' appearing upstairs, now, in busy streets like this, and on the Quays. Very expensive, though. At least a thousand a month to rent; for the smallest. Central, of course; but that never-ending noise? The air is laden with fumes. My throat is objecting to this on-going treatment. Perhaps a small respite?

A short by-pass to the corner of Church Street. A bloke whose name I can't remember used to own this pub when I lived near-hand. He was a famous Cavan footballer then - or recently retired. That was when the likes of Cavan had a football team. And such stalwarts still carried a certain awe, and mystique. 'Looked up to', you might say. The Gaelic man now has to be very exceptional indeed to be able to claw any of the adulation away from the almighty soccer 'hoods'.

Lincoln Place. A name to conjure with, as they say. Where some of the lawyers of our time sojourn, for a while, to learn the trade. What a money-making game it is, too, nowadays. There can't possibly be a better country in the world for the likes of them to 'clean-up'(or some of them). Legal complicity, in a country of extremes. An imposing little street, though.

It looks across at Bolton Street Tech. Also a school of learning, indeed, but one with less lofty ambitions, I suspect. And less lofty hopes of riches, for its inhabitants. I wonder if the boys and girls up in Lincoln Place sometimes look over and, rubbing their hands, wish for an endless supply of clients?

Where to next? Dorset Street beckons. Dorset Street: one memory is of having my very first taste of alcohol there. About '62. Never looked back, as they say; except in anger. Mostly old houses around here; in fine fettle though, I'd say. Like their clients; unceasing good form, it seems, and 'best foot forward', at all times. So close to the hub of things here; but still just far enough out to be un-bothered by the ceaseless movement of the out-of-town shopper.

The State cinema -just on the corner? No more. Can remember seeing a film called 'The Wild Bunch' there. Was it Bill Holden? Lee Marvin? No place for 'cissies' in Hollywood then, ha. And today they say that Katie Hepburn just died? There was a woman that didn't need no women's rights movement to get her way. Put herself and Bette Davis together and the world of men would go running. Thanks for the memories, State cinema. A lot of solicitors offices and such around, I notice. I suppose they have to go somewhere. Only kidding sir -honest.

Temple Street Childrens' Hospital just off the stroll. Many's the time we had to bring the little brats there, to receive their first-class service.

Drumcondra beckons. The Canal - Royal this time. Tolka Park around the corner; Bunny Fulham and Co.? Associations, eh?

Botanic Avenue on the left, leading to Cross Guns Bridge, and Phibsboro. That fine place:' the association for the blind' on the way. Wasn't there a big factory just across the canal here? Was it Wills Tobacco, or what? I'll think of it. Reminds me of the very large car factory that was in Portobello long ago? Again - beside canal, and half the length of Road; was it British Leyland? You won't find them situated locally anymore; have to be all clustered in estates, it seems. Anyway, that's how it goes. For now, I'll continue this stroll for another mile or two.

Eccles Street on the left, with all its associations. And the Mater, of course. A centre of sickness, you could say. Remember when being on their local radio there, getting lost coming out of it. All those endless corridors, with seemingly nothing going on. How much of it is really out of use, I wonder? On the left, the private parts, if you'll excuse the expression. Better not look that direction too long - they might charge me.

Back to Drumcondra. All those cars, on this fine road, heading north, mostly. Early departures, I suppose, from office and factory. Heading home, to the estate that holds all their family and dreams. The endless estates, strewn across the north-side sky. The drivers seem stressed; the days worries laid aside, but lingering on, as they slowly find a way through the traffic chaos. For now - Drumcondra is a conduit, to relative peace and quiet. Maybe I, too, should make my way in that direction?

Another 8 miles, maybe, but hey, I can do it. After all, walking is good for me, yeah? Griffith Avenue seems the best way, for the moment. At least, that way, I can pick up a bus, if I make it to Howth Road. What a fine long road it is, too. Such magnificent houses. You get the feeling they were there before the modern builder was given the nod to 'modernise'. Maybe it's most impressive feature is the line of trees, on both sides. Majestic. Pity the Corpo still have this compunction to move in on such a road as this, and come up with something to disrupt. They've put in endless bollards, all over the place, and jutting lumps of concrete, that completely ruins both the road, and the footpath. Why do they do it? It must cost a lot to do. Ye may have noticed something similar at the bottom of Talbot Street? Multiply that by a 100, and you've got the new Griffith. Anyway, I try to make the best of what's left. The long gardens, and the steps to the front door; the elegance of the venerable houses; the feeling of some history buried there. Looking from the end, there's a feeling of artistry in the layout; something akin to that Paris street.

There's Grace Park Road, running from Richmond all the way up to Beaumont. Since lately, the name has a different resonance for me: I had a decent win on two golfers, with the bookies, and one of the golfers was-and is-called Grace Park. God bless her little tootsies. Don't think she has much in common with Drumcondra, though - far as I know, she's from Korea. So many schools and such along here, -at least-just behind the road. A resident population, I expect, in splendid surroundings.

I reach the Malahide Road, and wait on a 32 bus. That continual pull between great intentions and the necessity borne of exhaustion can have only one result, as I again give into the reality of un-fitness. So, Killester, Raheny, Kilbarrack, Baldoyle slip slowly by as I peer out at them, with a declining interest. There is a probability of a brand new day raising its little promising head again in about twelve hours, and then will be time enough to traverse some more fascinating facsimiles of a changing town.

Unfamiliar Family

To be tenth out of twelve in a family means you are going to have some advantages, as well as the opposite.

First of all, as soon as you can walk, you will be given all the menial jobs. This may be running to the well, with an enamel bucket for fresh water; or bringing in endless bags of turf for the various fires. Or looking for duck eggs and hen eggs in ditches, and bringing them home - leaving just one, so that they won't abandon the nest. Also, when at the table, you will be given the leftovers; maybe a bone discarded by big brother; or a sausage, without the rasher. You will spend many moments looking from plate to plate, and getting very self-righteous indeed. You will be bossed by more than the Mum and Dad.

Oh yes. Those bigger and stronger will feel they have the right to use you as a slave, if not a battering ram. Maybe they just remember when they were your unfortunate size, and feel the time for retribution is at hand.

Advantages? Visiting relations will always be good to you. It may be no more than a few sweets; or maybe a half-crown from the Yank; or a visit to the circus; or the shops. Also, the Mum will - at least for a few years - bring you along when doing her shopping in the next town. All the rest will be left at home, which is the best part. She is yours for the day, and all that attention is surely good for the ego. It is also something you'll remember for a long time. You are like a curiosity for a while, in a way. Visitors will say things like: "he has his father's nose, God Bless him. And his sisters smile, the poor lúdramán." Or: "I wonder if he's the last?"

But what did I see, from the confines of my cot? Strangely, I was always very curious about the people around me. I was never sure if they were belonging to the house, or just more of those visitors that seemed to be forever coming and staying. Indeed, I was all of ten before I could definitely identify my sisters. Always away, they were - studying to be nurses, or some such.

Morning Glory.

There was a pram, of sorts. It had wobbly wheels, and a hard inside. I knew all about its insides.

It would be left in the kitchen, usually near the fire. With both doors open, though, so that there was plenty of fresh air to counteract the heat, don't you see.

The floor was cold, though. Anytime I was dumped on that floor, I wasn't a happy nappy-holder. Was it 'flags' they were called? The house I was born into was very much an old farmhouse type. Thick walls and small windows; though slates were used instead of thatch. It was surely a wonder to a lot of people where the heck we used all fit? To say 'three in a bed' would be no exaggeration. With some coming and going, though, it was hard to keep track of them all. When the Dad added a few more rooms later on, it was a big relief to all. Place to breathe again.

The makey-up bed over the kitchen was a favourite, though. It was got to by a rickety ladder, and anyone up there had a big advantage over those underneath, when it came to devilment.

But, the days passed quickly, and I found myself out of that pram, and in the bottom of a bed. To this day I hate the smell of people's feet. The mornings were the worst, though. When our Dad called you early it was wise to give in to his wishes. Within five minutes of his roar, the place would be chaotic. People running for turf; others gulping down porridge; others out for to collect the cows. Sure it was like panic stations. I was in no hurry to be joining that clan. Indeed, I found it a smart thing not to be in the firing line at all while they ran amok. A quiet corner was where to be, until the house quietened down.

Boiled eggs seemed to be what most of them ate. That and porridge. Me? I'd be given spoonfuls of all sorts by some of them. Mostly it was brutal, but they'd not stop until I'd swallow it, and so I got used to most foods I suppose, from a young age. Mum would give me a spoon of Cod Liver Oil every day, and that meant more very ugly faces from me, as I suffered the ignominy of that taste. The milk would always be warm - straight from the cow, of course.

Steps Outside

To be able to walk, I discovered, was a wonder. Wobbly, surely, and frequently on my behind; but slowly I was discovering what had been bothering me for a long time: what was going on outside?

I remember my first venture wasn't entirely happy, though. When the coast was clear, I pushed the back door open and it banged behind me. What greeted me? One big goose, that's what. It took one look at me and thought to itself: easy meat. The neck was extended and the beak opened as it went for me. It was probably my first taste of real fear. Boy did I cry. 'A roar to waken the dead', as my Dad used say. It worked though, and my Mum came to the rescue.

I had second thoughts about the vast outside after that. Next time, she brought me out. It was my first sight of what was to become such an important part of my working days, from then on. The farm-yard. Oh my, but it was a busy place - and smelly. It was later that I realised that smells and farm-yards go together.

It was like a big square that had this low-walled bit in the middle, and that was where all the smelly stuff was put. I hated that. There were stables all around. Some for cows, and some for horses, and so on. Indeed, there was a small one that had this big tub, and that was where all our own smells were put. We had to sit on it, trying not to fall in. To be honest, I thought I had the better deal, with my own little pot.

So, I was discovering; and questioning. My poor parents must have been sick of me, with my questions. I know they already had been through it all many times, but they said I was the worst. Guess I've reverted to my questioning mode again now ... with all this wandering back. It is fascinating, though, to rediscover more meanings to what I thought had been left far behind.

Sometimes, when I go back now, I'm inclined to look at everything with a different eye. What was the thing then that made me most mad? Or sad? And, more especially, why? Who were the people who had most influence? Why did I retain so much awe for the place? Will I discover any answers?

It is going to be a painstaking journey - but far from painful. I hope.

Bottled Memories

To re-enact a memory of Secondary School, is for me, just a little painful. For 1952 was very much a pre-enlightenment period. Some might say - so is 2010.

But, for a gasúr from the suburbs of Enniscrone, at such a time, going to 'boarding school' was very much a severe sentence, in my eyes. Even-though my experiences of National School were not exactly idyllic - with the daily reminders of our absolute worthlessness falling on our ears, knuckles, heads etc. from canes, rulers and fists. Indeed, my daily routine outside of school hours was also less than ideal, as my father had this thing about earning one's keep; and he was one who had perfected the art of delegation, before the word was heard of.

Still, St. Muredachs loomed on my burgeoning horizon, and come September, my old case was tied up with someone's leather belt, and I was on my way. What a sorry lot we must have seemed, trundling up that long driveway. Scrawny, hungry- looking, and devoid of all enthusiasm.

Being a first-year at that time was not a privileged position to be in, as we soon found out. Initiation ceremonies were entered into with wild abandon - by just about everybody that considered themselves above such things i.e. - all non first years. While we probably mostly entered into spirit of the thing, I think second and third years' chances of dunking our innocent little heads were given the thumbs down.

Routine was very soon imposed, and five years of study, classes, walking ''round the square', football, handball, table tennis, bed at ten, and mass at seven, was what was spread out in front of us for that eternity.

I remember that first class. I believe it was English, held by a Fr. Harrison, who gloried in the unflattering nick-name of:

Bon. Sweet, he was not; volatile…yes. But, as well as Irish, I seemed to take to the subject somehow.

I was surprised by the presence in our class of many more young fellas, who I'd not seen before. I learned that they were what were usually referred to as Day Boys. I don't think the collective 'we' took to them very well. They were more boisterous, more sure of themselves, and they could run home to their Mammy's every evening. Maybe the first two were qualities we quickly aspired to - but the third? Certainly not. After all - they were only 'townies', and not used to the realities of life; not like us hardened souls. Well - those of us from across the border, anyway.

Though, at this far remove, I can admit to having good friends then among that disparate lot - like Tom Courell, Pop McNamara, Pat Wynne, and Dui Halloran. Hunger is one thing that stuck in my mind about those days. The grub was never wholesome, and never plentiful. Growing bodies needed something more substantial, more filling - or fulfilling. That was where Ardnaree came in. I owe my very survival to that haven for the misbegotten. Climbing that wall was akin to climbing the Berlin Wall. Capture meant suffering, if not worse. Very few attempted it, but I - blessedly not having enough sense to refrain - and one other, maybe Sean Cawley from somewhere in the Nephin direction, or Tom Walshe, or maybe Tom Munnelly from Crossmolina - got into the habit of doing so. Several times Doc. Loftus stopped us when queuing to go back into study, and made us empty our pockets. Not once did a mere crumb even, show itself to the waiting eyes - and fists.

Our rare visits to the world outside were shepherded by the teachers, who had the heavy responsibility of looking after our tender selves. Quite right, too, considering the reported existence in Ballina of those occasions of glorious sin called 'wimin'.

So, final thoughts? It was harsh. Unforgiving. Of doubtful value. It was a product of its time. So were the teachers; they were slaves to a pathetic curriculum. I'm aware that things quickly improved, later. But, those memories don't - thankfully - impose. What really lingers are the laughs, the friendships, and the crazy long-ago times. A very different world, then, and one I'm very glad to have been part of.

As I think of having lived through the old country life of horses, flails, and binders; the old city life of horses, cattle thundering through Stoneybatter to the fairs; and pigs at the end of gardens; the Sunday walk to Croke Park. Then the new lives of both city and country, where technology and sophistication have bidden my old memories to the archives. Getting through such a life is, in itself, a hardship. But, to attempt it without the benefit, dodgy though it sometimes be, of a secondary education, would be surely a helluva lot worse.

So - St. Muredachs? Thanks for the memories.

And thanks for listening too, you lot.

Darkness

They surrounded my
youth, the old ways.
A mere pup in that isle of dogs,
licking the scattered bones.
Reared at the deathbed
of an ancient way of life.
Its thoughts, its moods,
seeped into my soul.
The stiff black suits of Sunday;
Cast in desperate devotion.
The un-shared power of the
head-of-house; majestic
mothers, carrying the battle
to their graves; and the children
carrying their anxieties
into another world.
Bangs on the ear from all-powerful
teachers. Wagging fingers of priests;
gaunt figures of neighbours
with tales of war, and want.
They trespassed on my dreams.
Now the shadows have lifted
and I can see that strange time
in a clearer light.

Grave Doubts

It's time to stop and listen close.
Our centuries chasing to a close.
Our country too, is growing old;
So much we've bought; so much we've sold.

It would be good to listen still,
To voices from the gravely ill.
To hear the words from good and bold;
Who came and went, while still 'on hold'.

How to make the big break-through?
To find words from the silenced few?
But soon, the challenge was well met;
They streamed in on the internet.

Elbowing in first, was Dev, the dour.
Said he: 'I fear this earth tastes sour,
And your callins not just what they were.
But ye're politics? Oh dear. Oh dear.'

Mickín Collins inched in then. Laughed he:
'did ya hear that fecker? Moanin' still?
It's gas down here; but not really
Sure I haven't met one decent hoor.

Then Bernie Shaw came roaring through.
Still hadn't shaved; but then - would you?
He said: 'I see that poetry's quite the thing?
Who would have thought, with our thin skin?'

Next up pops Jimmy Joyce, on cue.
Looking pert, and sharp; unhappy, too.
Sez: 'dear friends and artists, - make no haste
To come mix with masters—with no taste.'

Then came 'the master' strolling in.
All pensive like, stroking his chin.
'Just a warning friends, and it beats me hide,
but here, all Kerry men play for the other side.'

Costello came, to add to the mix,
Intent on settling some fervent fix, but sez:
'It's good, I'm sure to have my thoughts shared
But I'll hold my brief, as I've nothing prepared'.

Of course ould Yeats had to do his stuff;
With eye-glass, scowl and pinch of snuff.
We thought his words would surely be long
But all he croaked was: Is Maude gone?

With that, the screen went very blank;
An end was brought, with ne'er a thank.
All heads and souls returned to base
Where silence makes a better case.

Imelda

An artist, a dreamer,
A beauty; a woman.
With an artist's instinct,
She sought her own space.

She found her El Dorado
In the quiet countryside of Clare.
A place to relax the mind;
To finally be herself.

To be alone when she wished.
To paint; to rear her family.
Other artists too, added to
The ambience of this 'commune'.

But this Irish idyll
Also contained its snake.
Shielding her beloved child, she
Died at the hands of a cruel fate.

Though not knowing her, I grieve.
I grieve too for what we've lost.
Is there nowhere left, in this tired world,
To escape to, to be free?

Her

I wallow in her presence
Smile in our sharing
Share in our fellowship
Love in her bearing.

She is Easter in winter
A smile in a tear
A help when I'm helpless
A consoling prayer.

She is Rita forever
A Curtin supreme
A real Limerick siren
With some Dublin cream.

A wife that's not bossy
A mother that vows
A cook without equal
A woman that wows.

She's my plus in the minus
The hope in the dread
The promise of springtime
When all buds are dead.

I'm in love forever
And always will be
But when I turn eighty
Will she still love me?

Conquistador

Timothy was not one for days out. When Sara said they were all going for a picnic, he was not really interested. 'Not my cup of tea.' he said, grinning from ear to ear.

Ben, being three, came up with the perfect answer: "You could have a coffee, Uncle Tim." sez he, with the foresight of an elder. "Please come, please?" For Timothy was a popular cad with the youngsters.

Sera or Tom certainly had trouble trying to analyse why. To them he was a nuisance. Simply that. He would come visit - and stay. Not that they ever put too much pressure on him to do so. Oh no - it was the kids - Ben and Ann that did that.

How he liked to play his little games, too. Protest within their earshot, for instance. Say things like: 'Ah, I'd love to, but sure your parents have far too much to be doing to be bothered with the likes of me." Then they would do the pleading. Of course he'd come with presents for them.

Sera said to Tom once: "I suppose it would never occur to him to bring a bag of groceries home at some time, after one of his wanderings."

"Not bloody likely." said Tom.

But the 'day out' was planned, and was going ahead, with or without their visitor. Baskets packed into the car, and all the rest of the necessary paraphernalia. Tim 'gave in' at the last minute. He even packed his pockets with bottles of stout, to help him through the day. Sera thought she got a glimpse of a naggin of whiskey, peeping out of the inside pocket.

The destination was a valley, not too far away. It was ideal, really; having many fine trees, and a river through it. The kids liked to climb the trees, and boast of the great heights reached. Tom talked of how his father used to bring him there too; and of the grand and happy memories he had of it all. Sera reminded him of how they used also pay the odd visit there, when doing their 'courting'. "Begod. 'tis different memories you have, so." said Tim, with just a hint of envy.

"Isn't it strange you never married yourself?" said Sera.

"Strange? What's strange about it?" he asked.

" I'm sure there must have been some women in your life at some time." said she.

"And if there was itself, what business is it of yours?"

Tom and Sera looked at him with surprise. It sounded like a raw nerve had been touched. Maybe our 'hard man' had an Achilles heel after all?

Tim opened his first bottle, offering one to Tom as well. He took it.

"Love can be a dangerous article sometimes." said Tom, smiling.

"Well can it now?" said Tim, not really biting.

" Ah go on." sez Sera. "Tell us all of your conquests. I'm sure the kids would love to hear all about them."

"Yeah-yeah-yeah. Uncle Tim's conquests..." shouted both Ann and Ben.

"What's conquests, Mum?" whispered Ann. "SSHHH." sez she.

"Come down to the river, kids, and I'll teach ye how to tickle a trout." said Tim.

"He's wriggling out of it, I'd say." said Tom.

"Embarrassed, sure, the poor man." offered Sera.

There followed a silence. Another bottle was opened; sandwiches consumed; tea poured. A swig of whiskey was called for, and badly needed too.

"Conquests is right. " ventured Tim. "Sure 't would take all day to tell ye of all of them."

"Not your typical 'lady-killer', though, I'd say." smiled Tom.

"Begod you're well able for the nasty remark, Tom, I notice- for all your niceness."

"Let's keep it civil, if you please." suggested Sera, afraid that things could so easily get out of hand. "Don't be sad, uncle Tim." pleaded Ann, touching his hand.

A tear welled up in his eye, and he hugged little Ann. "I wonder do ye know how lucky ye are." he said, looking over at Tom and Sera.

"Come on kids, - let's go down to the river." shouted Sera, figuring it was time to call an end to the little drama.

And so, the day went its quiet way. No more was said, and Tim took his leave the following day. He never came and stayed again; though visits did take place. Both Tom and Sera agreed that 'maybe he wasn't such a bad ould soul after all'. Misunderstandings too often cloud the issue, for want of a civil word.

Winding By

Sometimes it seems as if my life is governed by literature, or something to do with it.

When The Winding Stair was closing its doors I felt compelled to wander in - of course on the last day. I felt a sorrow at its passing; as I'd done a few years earlier when a very similar shop in Sligo closed down. I wandered around, taking in its almost musty atmosphere, and its, to me, priceless reality.

Even the stairs itself - windy indeed, and the original, contained notes and quotes and things to make you stop and read. There was a large poem from the estimable Pat Ingoldsby on the wall. I recalled when I last talked to him on Howth Pier. I'd mentioned the fact to him. He reached behind one of his boxes and gave me a copy of it.

Upstairs - the tea-rooms. A place to relax and savour the moment - whether observing the passing trade, or parade, outside, and on the new sidewalks; or, better still, to browse through that book you just got, downstairs.

Downstairs, where quick exits are an unlikely occurrence. I was determined, on that final day of its public availability, to leave with more than memories. For a quid each, I got hold of several very old magazines and such.

On the top floor I found more-more specific-books of maybe academic interest. And on the walls, framed memories. One in particular a record of when I and two other 'chancers' did our thing before a packed room, for about 35 minutes each. It was part of the Emerging Poets business, organised by Poetry Ireland. Quite a memory.

This past Sunday was another of those kind of days for me. As part of the Theatre Festival, a play about the great Laurel and Hardy was on in the Olympia, and this was something we both did not want to miss. It was wonderful, and so well done. A lot of nostalgia, and laughter.

More memorable for me, was the chat I had with the elderly barmaid in the place - it being necessary to pass a little time before settling. She it should be said, was of the old brigade and fortunate was I to have her to myself, as it were, for a little while. Our conversation varied from an outgoing customer: 'Jaysus. If she smiled her face would fall off.' To the delights of Bray and the great meal she had the last time she was there. Her meal? - fish and chips. 'Me life on you,' I thought. But her expression suggested that the departed customer had left an unfortunate lasting impression. 'Too many of them around today, and they surly.' sez she.

We then covered various other topics, all in the space of ten minutes. Including the Limerick lady what won the money. She should leave that house,' she said. 'Leave it as it is-and get far away from there.'

To me, those are the magical moments, and such as she magical people. I like to support the Olympia and have often done so, even monetarily. It and The Gate are very special places. Afterwards we wandered, as we like to do, particularly, when in the city.

Temple Bar was busy, but I felt somehow out of touch with it. During the day, it seems to me, it's a place to wander around and count the nationalities. Maybe pick up something really good in the market; but at night it is a place to get sick in.

I was soon saved from alienation by the welcome sight of a bookshop. Blessedly, old books again. How I browsed the shelves, with every moment endowed with the possibility of something special popping out and grabbing my choosy attention. It is enough to say that I left with two little gems, at two quid each.

One was: *Of Human Bondage* by the one and only Mr Maugham. The other: *On the Sea of Cortez* by a man who was my most favourite writer through my extended youth - John Steinbeck. Two different type of chaps no doubt, but to read their stuff is to learn. Sometimes a day can turn special, just on a whim.

All the way home I hugged those books; those memories ... even the wife.

Done Dancin'

Doyle was fully convinced that his chosen life-style was the only one possible for a free spirit like himself. He put out his third cigarette and got off the bed.

He hated Sundays. Sundays are the kinda time when a man's patience is tested to the full, in his opinion. There's the church bells in the morning, for a start. Taunting him, they were. The Sunday papers were no better; with their cheap CDs, and cheap headlines.

'An insult to a thinking man.' - that's how he summed them up.

And the bloody pubs closed until twelve. The devil be with the days when you had to get out by 2.30 and twiddle your thumbs 'til 4.

At least now there was a decent time to work on a proper hoor of a headache.

He thought of Deborah again. Would he ring her? He put a clatter of Jameson into the coffee, and sat down .

'Decisions are a bastard betimes,' he decided.

He rang her. 'Howya Deborah. Nice to hear your voice again.'

'Considering that the last time you heard it, it was arguing with you, that surprises me.'

'Ara, what's an argument but a communication of ideas between friends?'

'Jaysus Doyle, what's this? Feckin philosophy - and on a Sunday morning. 'You're in a good mood today - have ya someone there with ya?'

'Suspicious bastard, aren't you. What if I had? Is it any of your business?'

'None at all.'

'What are you ringing me for?'

'I was thinking of you, that's all.'

'Well were you now. Thinking of how you'd treated me so badly all this time, and how, now that you find you can't get on without me, maybe you should make some half-hearted attempt to make it up to me? Is that what you were thinking, hmmm? '

'No.'

'Frig off Doyle.'

'Do you like me at all?'

'That's a tough one. Do I like you? Do I like this Neanderthal man whose life surrounds the portals of the nearest pub? A Neanderthal who likes to live in the past of the Irish bachelor, when the world was uncomplicated and people hadn't yet acquired this nasty habit of 'moving on', and acquiring a smatter of sophistication? Do I like that man at all? Do you really want to know?'

'Yes.'

'Let me ask you something, Doyle. What do you want from me? And don't say, or think: a good time and a good meal. I know your mind, you little bastard.'

'Want? I want the same as you, Deborah. I want friendship. I want the best bloody friendship ever existed between man and woman on this shit of a rock called earth. Is that too much to ask? Is it?'

'And what would this 'friendship' consist of, Doyle? Hmmm? Would it consist of the same as before? Where the hallelujah of a night out, would be a laugh with 'the boys' and me. A night of football and strong language? Of strong booze and bad manners? Of limited chances and limited possibilities? Of the fifties re-visited? Where the idea of film or theatre or music or dance is as far away as it is possible to be? Or do you envisage a friendship of different hues, perhaps? Hmm?'

'Jaysus, I didn't think you thought so little of me. You enjoyed being out with me. Admit it.'

'Did I? Really? Enjoy - mmmm? I wonder if you mean I laughed at your jokes, and indulged you, and your friends. Even to the extent of fervent laughter. Or do you mean, I was so taken with your very presence, that merely to be near you was sufficient to make me the happiest and luckiest girl on the planet?'

'Yeah, that one's closer.'

'Do you know what you are, Doyle? You're a piss-pot.'

'So ya do still like me, then?'

'Come on, out with it. What do you want of me this time?'

'Going for a drink?'

'Any specific reason why I should?'

'I want to clear up this business about Jolie and me; I mean our misunderstanding of all that business.'

'That I'd like to hear - Doyle grovelling. The usual place, I suppose? See you at twelve then'.

Doyle let out a loud 'YES...' - as soon as the phone was down.

He was there first, and surveyed the scene. Tosser Flynn was there already and attacking the first pint with a vengeance. He threw an eye at Doyle without an acknowledgement. Doyle joined him at the bar.

'Howya Tosser.' sez he.

'What the hell are you doin' here?' was the response.

'Look.' said Doyle, deciding to confront the issue. 'We all seem to have fallen out over this business with Jolie. Let me tell ya one thing, right? She was the one started it. Started comin' on to me, so she did. At first, I thought I was imagining it, so I did; but it continued. So I thought: 'Feck it. Let's call her bluff. See how far she'll go, like? No better man, wha'? So I do, and she lit on me. Ya know the rest. You can believe me or not, Tosser - but that's the way it was.'

'I'll tell ya something here now, Doyle.' said Tosser assuming a serious pose. 'She tried the same thing wit' me. Sure as hell.

I thought: what's the story, like? This fine looking bird trying it on with me? What's her game, like? 'Told her to piss off, Doyle. True as Gawd. So I believe ya, right?'

Doyle was dumbfounded, or something. He knew that Tosser had been many things in his lifetime. But somehow the thought of this booze-bellied bald sixty year old, as a 'lady-killer' didn't seem to fit. Now if he was a fine specimen like himself, then Doyle would have taken the idea seriously.

Just then, Deborah came in. She was all dressed up, and Doyle was mightily impressed. 'Jaze. You're lookin' great, girl. What are ya havin'?'

'I'll have a Bacardi and Coke, just as I always have, ok?'

'Coming up. You want to get a seat? Or is the bar good enough for you?'

'Since we have such serious things to discuss Doyle, like your list of silly excuses for instance, we'd better have a little privacy, don't you think? No offence, Tosser.'

'Yer alright, girl. But I thought you'd got sense and dumped this chancer.'

'That is still to be resolved. See you later.'

'Christ, Tosser. You're not being much help.'

'Look, I'm only speaking me mind, right? What a fine girl like her is doing with a time-waster like you is beyond me.'

'Beyond you? Jaze; sure everything's beyond you. A Bacardi and Coke there, Jimmy, please, along with that pint.'

'Coming up Mr. Doyle. Come here 'til I tell you something, though. Isn't it about time you done the decent thing and married that girl?'

'Married? For frigs sake, Jimmy, will ya keep your voice down.'

'What d'you think Tosser?'

'I think any girl that'd marry that buck would be to be pitied.'

'Now ye all know that I'm the confirmed bachelor, and nothing in this world will change that.'

'Every married man in this city used think the same thing, I can tell ya. When the claws go into ya, there's little ya can do. Take it from me.'

'Well, you can concentrate on Tosser here; because I'm me own man. See ye later.'

He goes to join Deborah 'What was Jimmy saying to you?'

'Ara, he was gas-baggin' out of him. Never mind.'

'So - out with it, then? Your grovelling starts here.'

'There'll be no grovelling from me. I have my genuine excuses, so I have.

'Which are?'

'Well, you know how we split up because of what was supposed to be going on with me and Jolie? Right. Well, the thing is - and this is the god's truth - she was the one that started it.'

'So ?'

'Well, I mean to say. It wasn't me like. I was innocent of any instigations.

'So - you're saying that Jolie 'came onto' you, and dragged you to her bed.

'Now don't be making it worse than it was, Deborah. There was no bed or any that stuff, at all at all.'

'Much to your disgust, Doyle. You tried it on with her, right? Now where lies your innocence in all of this?'

'Fair enough. But I was only calling her bluff, Deb. That's all.'

'But if she had gone along with it? Then what?'

'Well , I mean to say. That's not a fair question, is it? She didn't, like.'

'Out with it, Doyle. Would you have shagged her if you got the chance?'

'Look. You're the only woman in my life Deborah, and the only one I ever loved.'

'Loved, did you say? That's a new one alright. Getting desperate, are we?'

'Look I mightn't have told ya before, like; but it's true. Mad about ya, I am. True as God.'

'So - having shown your true feelings for me, you now might like to do me the honour of answering my question.'

'I suppose. If she was insistent like and really on for it, I'd maybe, ya know like not want to. Ya know yerself, not want to disappoint her, like.

'Say it, Doyle. Say it.'

'Alright.... course I would.'

'You bastard. You two-timing bad-minded useless son of a bitch.'

'What? I only said what you wanted to hear.'

'You could have said No. Don't you know anything? Jesus.'

'I think you're over-reacting a bit here, Deb.'

'Oh do you now? I'll show you over-reacting . You and I are finished, and I can assure you this is for good. Goodbye Doyle.' She leaves.

Doyle is disconsolate, or thinks he is. He tries to figure out just what happened. 'Woman is desperate.' he thinks to himself. 'Desperate to the world.'

He sits by himself for a while. That smile on Tosser's face shouldn't be given any succour, he figures. Then, who comes in but Jolie, with some new bloke with her. Then Prancer McGowan, looking like he'd barely survive until that first slug of stout got into him. They all sit at the bar and the usual craic starts. Doyle had no stomach for it, but leaving after one pint wasn't on either. He thought of going somewhere else, when Jolie said, loud enough: 'Well, well. If it isn't Mr. Doyle. And all alone. I wonder why?'

'Dark forces at work, Jolie. Some people has it in for him, I hear.' said Tosser.

Prancer started laughing. 'Begod, that Deborah one can be a handful, I'd say.'

'Another pint, Doyle?' asked Jimmy. 'You look like you need it.'

Though Doyle knew that this was Jimmy's way of keeping the show on the road, he said smartly enough: 'Alright so, Jimmy. Seeing as it's on the house.' He moved to the bar, and sat.

'Well? What's your next move, boy? I'd say that's you and Deborah finished, like.' This from Prancer, who knew all about married life and the necessity of hanging onto the 'old values'.

'Well, Prancer,' said Doyle, now imbued with a degree of gravitas; 'While I recognise your experience and all that shit in the area of how to treat women, Irish style as in the 1950's, for instance, I still question your knowledge of how things are today. You might get away with your lifestyle- as does Tosser. But I'm a man who recognises the importance of treating people right. Now, where me and Deborah goes from here is our business, and only ours. I'll leave ye now, and hope that my absence doesn't ruin the proceedings. By the way Jolie, I notice you didn't introduce your latest friend. All I can say to you, friend, is this: Watch her. She has a thing about older men. Isn't that right, Tosser?'

With that, the bould man left, leaving the remaining to gather their defences.

Down There For Dancin

She was fifty-seven when the thought struck her.

A life of servitude and dedication had never before left time for pleasurable thoughts. Indeed, their unforced absence afforded her a life of blissful knowledge of the poor and unfortunate happenings to all those around her; even if they interspersed with mere moments of counter-balancing.

Gertrude was a woman of high moral fibre, and no mistake. Indeed, she even favoured the high fibre content of a muesli breakfast, knowing that while a mind that played the game of intelligent procrastination and deliberate avoidance was only beneficial to the soul if accompanied by a body that was well behaved. Then the sudden disappearance through death of all those to whom her life had been betrothed biblically, left her with an empty void. That void was peered into on occasion. It was a Thursday morning. Sky was at least less than grey.

The absolute ablutions had been tended to. Her hand went for that cloth and Kleenex with which to clean the windows. Then she saw that next to it was the cloth with which she would clean the floor; then the towel to clean the dishes. Near hand was the hoover. Her whole day was lined up in a corner just waiting for the dutiful hand to use. The hours waiting too, in tandem.

It was then she remembered the void - the empty one, in another unspecified corner. It seemed to offer choice.

Gertrude got a cup of tea and sat down. There was conflict straight away. It's nearly 10 o'clock. You can't sit down. What about the jobs, the duties.?'

Momentary fright. Guilt attempted entry. Then that golden moment. The blinding light struck and she found a new she; a long-suffocating she that had longed for a voice all her life. She now emerged and took over.

"Ya know what, jobs, ya know what 'duties? Ya can bog off for good. Ya hear?"

She threw the tea into the fireplace, filled a glass with left-over spirit, and tossed her shoes in the air. 'From now on,' she told herself, 'she was gonna bath in brandy, sail in Salamanca, toddle in Tasmania; go crafty in Corfu. She was gonna seduce some fat rich Greek in a jacuzzi.

She, Gertrude the Free, was gonna fill that void.

Enjoyment

'Are ya ready yet?' she asked.

'I'm ready.' I answered.

'Come on then.'

She was already out the door; the taxi driver waiting at the gate. I had one last look around, feeling sure of something missing. Even locked the inside doors, out of habit. Checked my keys. Nervous reactions, probably. Not used to leaving home for long stages. Three weeks being long, for me.

She called again ... 'Will ya hurry up.'

It always appears to be the job of the female to get others to 'hurry up.' To be there at least two hours before need be; 'ya cannot be too careful, anything could happen,' and such words of doubtful wisdom, are automatic.

I waited for the driver to ask where we were going, etc.

Hairdressers do that too. 'Been on yer holiers yet?' will emanate after the first flash of scissors across your balding mane. Before she, or he, finishes, you know of all their past outings and future plans. I never know what exactly I'm likely to answer, as the mere truth is somehow usually a let-down. So it may be exotic...like Madeira; or erotic...like Carrahubbock by the Sea.

Of course, with a 'her' there beside you -the probability is you'll get to say nothing. Maybe an occasional 'mmmmm'. You become aware of yer man checking in the mirror to verify your assent, or dissent.

Arrival at airport is the start of 'no going back.' Checking in, at some blank and nameless screen seems like a pathetic descent into modernism - something I view usually 'as to be avoided'. At least the young lady can smile viciously as she piles on the extra charges. Then the inevitable coffee; and that first sign of holiday - the mucky cake.

You view the crowd around; from the stilettoed, to the ham-fisted; the wow - isn't this marvellous, to the 'Jaysus I bet it'll be rainin'. You find your place on the plane, and let her have the window seat. The buck beside you already has the crosswords out.

Nearly three hours since you left house, and still on the ground. You find a wish to be home just fleeting across the mind; but know that there is now no escaping it. Smiles and appreciation have preference over all other feelings; you'd best remember that.

Weak beer, rice with everything, English humour, pot-bellies, and ponsie beach bums are all a part of your holiday, chum. And you can write the script now for when you return: 'Our holiday? Sure it was great, so it was - marvellous!'

Faces, Places and Enduring Traces

Being someone who is not easily impressed by 'names' as such, I still must admit that I have met some people in my time that have impressed me. Not necessarily by anything brilliant they may have said to me, but by things already achieved in the public eye. Invariably, I've found them to be without any airs and graces, and easy to talk to.

One such was a man called Michael Morris - known to the world as Lord Killanin. How in the name of crackers did I manage to meet him, you may well ask? Well it wasn't while trying to negotiate a better deal for Ireland in the Olympics, I'm afraid - though I did try for a free ticket. It was while working in his home and office in Lansdowne Road, some time ago. He wanted a new, up-to-date telephone system, and I was the one with the job. Sometimes, when I'd arrive in the early morning, he would be on his exercise bike, trying desperately to keep in some kind of shape. He was so courteous and easy to get on with; and seemingly nonplussed by all the heavy workload he had on his plate at that time.

His secretary was a different kettle of barracuda's entirely. Indeed, I got the impression he didn't always get on too well with her and her over-fussy nature. Last time I met him, I was calling back some time later for some fault or other. He was coming out the door as I arrived. He greeted me, and throwing his eyes to heaven said: 'she's downstairs.'

He was a real gentleman, and I was proud to know him. One regret I did have was that I failed to get any tip from his son - Mouse Morris.

When in England in the sixties, I was visiting London, and walking down some street or other - could it have been Abbey Road? The bird with me said with bated breath, 'look who's coming down the road.' I recognised very quickly none other than - the Beatles. Four of them, and not a lot of fuss being made of them. No way was I going to let them pass without saying something. So we walked towards them and I said: 'Hi lads. Any chance of an autograph?' One of them, I think John said: 'You're Irish, yeah?' I said: 'Of course, are ya jealous?' They laughed, and I believe it was Ringo said: 'Hey. We're Irish too - well half Irish.' The bird asked: 'Which half?' After some smart retort from Lennon, Ringo said: 'Paul and John.'

Anyway, none of us had any paper for an autograph, and so McCartney gave me a card with their photograph on it, and his signature. Then they were gone. It all took only a minute or too, but I remember it so clearly. I still have the card. As I say, it was early in their career, and they weren't such a big deal at that time. But they were to me, and still are.

Who else? Well, in about the early sixties, I'm not at all sure of the year, I was in the vicinity of Stephens Green one afternoon and dropped into the big church on the north side of it. Strangely, it is something I rarely would do now, but maybe then I was more open to influences? Or maybe less cynical? Anyway, there I was, with very few others, and making my pitch when I noticed in the seat in front of me a form that was vaguely familiar in profile. I looked closer and realised there was only one man had a head like that - the one and only Dev. There was one other bloke beside him, possibly a bodyguard, though he had no uniform. I thought it too good a chance to miss; so I took out my colt 45 - no, no, no. I tapped him on the shoulder. He looked around. I apologised for annoying him, figuring that might buy me a few extra seconds if he was not in a receptive mood. I said I just wanted to shake his hand. I did so, and he asked my name. I told him, and said I was from Sligo. He asked if I was anything to Edward Hannon? I said yes, I'm his son. He thought for a minute and said: 'I thought he was a Mayo man?' I realised why he thought that my Dad was something or other in some command post in the North Mayo Brigade of the IRA. He obviously knew him or knew of him. I explained that that area of Sligo came under the North Mayo brigade, and he said 'I see.' Anyway, there was some further little chat and I said goodbye. He said to 'say hello to your Dad,' and I went. Thing is, I don't ever remember telling him. I hope I did. At the time I don't think I thought too much of the event. As a comparative youngster, I was probably not too easily impressed by anyone. But later, when remembering, I realised that, like or loath him, that guy was probably one of the biggest players in my country's history. And my meeting with him that quiet day in University Church was an event to remember. Mind you, though completely a-political, at least in the sense that I don't see the point of supporting one specific party, no matter what they do; but if I had the choice, I would have loved to meet Michael Collins.

What a loss he was to our country. Though I wonder too, how he would have survived and dealt with that dirty little game called politics? Anyway I didn't meet him. I met the 'survivor.'

Anymore? Any other well-known bleeders who were lucky enough to meet me. Well, a few. I was usually given the job of looking after the phones in some of the 'big houses' around the city. One such was Farmleigh. Yes, that place that they wanted to sell for around 19 mill. So our government decided: yeah-we'll buy it. So they gave 29 million for it, for starters.

Anyway, about 15 years ago I was out there for a couple of weeks, and mixing with the Guinness clan and so on. After all, I probably paid enough on my own towards their shopping bills over the years to qualify for a share of the place. Yer man more or less kept to himself, though he would occasionally bless us with a word.

There were many others I worked for while in the telephone game who were most impressive, though I can't honestly remember their names. Faceless people who were involved in the industry of our country, and making their companies work and making work for their country's employees - against the odds of restrictive taxes and impossible paper work.

I've always had an admiration for the employers of our country, on a general basis since those days. They are the ones who have the responsibility of making industry work, and of producing our vast exports every year. Including our farmers, by the way. Do you realise that we export about ten times more than we eat each year?

It galls me to hear politicians take credit for the state of our finances, or whatever; when all they basically contribute are hurdles for it to cross. It hardly needs saying that the employees are the ones at the coal-face, and in Ireland they have to be about the best there is. There endeth my anti - political broadcast.

When I was a kid, in my short pants and canvas shoes, I would often stop and talk to this old man on the way home from school. His name was Freddie Gannon, and he would usually be sitting on his low wall outside his little house. He would talk to me like he would to any adult, and be interested in anything I had to say. This memory has stayed with me all my life - perhaps more as an appreciation of him and his character, and his ability to communicate with kids. In those days, that was a rare gift. He lived beside another character we called Mickey the Cobbler, down a little lane-way; and if you were collecting shoes, or just dropping in to talk when the two of them were together, you could be sure of banter and fun to match any available from the best writers of comedy. That's what I call 'golden memories'.

Next door was a man called George Helly. He had a bicycle shop, and also fixed radios, charging up the batteries and whatever needed doing. He was a loveable character. He was a joker, and the first I knew who had an endless supply of jokes. He was also a great golfer, in the days when such a game was restricted to the few - and very few of those were any good.

Once, he had this new type of ball called a Dunlop 65 - just out. Well, on one round when I and my pal Christy were going around with him (maybe caddying), he lost it. He said to us that he would give us half a crown if we found it. I can tell you that we were not going to leave that course until we did so. After about an hour, we did find it. We split the half-dollar and had the time of our lives. I salute you George, and also Freddie and Mick. The three of them certainly brightened up the forties for me.

Impressive people? Sometimes it is only necessary to look close to home. Of course there are many others deserving of a mention. Hundreds maybe. But for now, that's probably enough.

Who would I like to meet , or to have met? That's a question that will take even more consideration. Straight off I can think of a few. In the film world, for instance, there's Paul Newman - mainly because of his work outside of film. Ingrid Bergman - for less obvious reasons. Patricia Neal. In the drama world: John Kavanagh, Arthur Miller, Donal McCann and Brenda Fricker. In poetry: maybe Emily Dickenson, Robert Frost, Wendell Berry. In music: Bob Dylan, Miles Davis, Ella Fitzgerald, Eric Burden, Jimi Hendrix. Writers? Steinbeck, Faulkner, O'Connor, Dostoevsky. In life in general: I'd like to have known my Dad as a younger man.

Achievements in my life? Maybe the biggest one so far is to have reached 71. In work, maybe not a lot. I always looked on work as no more than a way to earn money. I'd do it diligently, of course, and conscientiously; but never as a downright career. Fair enough - when younger, and in England, I was doing particularly well; even offered the job of supervising all the contracts across the Midlands. But of course I turned it down and came back to Ireland instead. Or at least to Northern Ireland. Though I stayed at the telephone game in one way or another for about 35 years, I really never considered it too seriously as a career. But it was fun, challenging, and it gave me a living.

On the sporting front, I was always involved in something or other: Gaelic football, handball, table tennis, golf and squash. I loved the football - as long as it lasted; was practically unbeatable at handball, though I never played at the Croke Park courts. I discovered squash only when a few courts opened in our local area; it is a fantastic game, I think - and demands fitness. Let's say the best I did at it was to get to league three - down from ten. But it's probably golf that I got to enjoy most.

I was born across a field from the first tee in Enniscrone, so it was hard to avoid. This past year is the first one since then, I've played very little of the game. Just giving it a rest. Nowadays, the best I could play to would be about 18 handicap - and that after a lot of practice. My greatest achievement in it was to play for Enniscrone in what was called The Connacht Shield, in about '64 or so. It was our first time entering, and for a very good reason. We only had about 11 playing members, or at least 11 that actually were any use at all. Problem was we had to pick a team of 8. And this against clubs that had around 200 playing members generally. It was a knock-out competition, and we finally won it out. The excitement in the town was unbelievable after each win. The final was on a home and away basis against Galway; and we won it on the last game. We went on to the all-Ireland semi-finals, and lost that by 4 games to 6. It was a tremendous achievement for a little club that had a poor enough 9 hole course; hardly any members, and no support. That success, though, led to unbelievable interest generally, and a very fine 18 hole course was finally opened by the great Christy O Connor himself, (Snr -that is). I should add that my partner Mark and myself only lost one game in the whole tournament. We were both good at match-play, as against stroke play; and had practised greatly for it. Sport-wise, it is a golden memory; and I am proud of it.

First Legs

I suppose watching a film is a fascination we all have, as well as being mostly an enjoyable experience. It is an escape mechanism, in a way. It is 'handy' to simply go into a cinema, and, for a few Euro enter the manufactured world of Hollywood, or maybe Pinewood.

It must have been exciting in the early days for those far-seeing makers of dreams. One thing they must have understood perfectly was the enormous variation in people's tastes. From love stories to horror stories. Of course, as we know, those two strangers sometimes merge - maybe that's when they called in Bette Davis? But, the brave move from 'silent' to 'talkies 'must have had many consequences .

It is well known that many actors and actresses had unsuitable voices, maybe squeaky, or hoarse. A premature end to a blooming acting career because of the sound of their voice, couldn't have been an easy thing to swallow. Obviously, now, we are not so sensitive to voice. Think of Mr. Schwarzenegger.

But how did this amazing business all start? Well, we've all heard of Thomas Alva Edison, I'm sure; the man who first came up with the phonograph? Plus a lot more. In 1894, he also put together a yoke called a Kinetoscope. It looked like a wooden case, fitted with an eyepiece at easy viewing height. Very soon, places called 'kinetoscope parlours' started to spring up, in which these devices would be put, and people soon started to queue up in droves to view. They simply put in a coin, and could view a short series of animated pictures, mounted on an endless belt, and lasting about a minute. Each machine had different pictures: from boxing matches, dances, music-hall scenes, comic sketches, and historical re-constructions. You can imagine the new Edison factories in West Orange, New Jersey, working day and night to keep the machines going. A special film studio - the first, was built, and it was nick-named the 'Black Maria'. Also, a very large factory, run by Edison's assistants William Kennedy and Laurie Dickson, and it's remit was simply: moving pictures.

The earlier Kinetograph used the flexible celluloid, developed by Eastman, which had lateral perforations to ensure the film moved smoothly past the shutter. However, he considered that the picture obtained was not good enough to project on a screen. Hence, the Kinetoscope. This had a simple mechanism - a film approximately 17 metres long, attached to an endless belt which turned continuously, thanks to a dynamo. The first actual film, lodged for copyright with the Library of Congress was called 'Edison Kinetoscope Record of a Sneeze' The 'star' was a man called Fred Ott, as he sneezes straight at the camera. It is recorded in 12 shots.

After all this, things started to move quickly. Jean Acme Leroy came up with the Cinematograph. The Lumiere brothers moved things along. Charles Pathé got involved. All this in 1895. Laurie Dickson set up on his own too. It appears Mr. Edison from then on spent a lot of time and money trying to protect his rights, and the rights to his patent. But things were moving along at a fast rate, and film was becoming more sophisticated by the year.

By 1900, at the World's Fair, Louis Lumiere had a giant screen installed, that was 15 by 25 metres, and visible to 25,000 people. The fight between Jim Jeffries and Thomas Sharkey was filmed. 1800 metres of film was used - up to 30 minutes film.

In Britain, Robert William Paul from Southgate, was getting in on the act, as well. He had his own factories, and endless supply of props. He started with mostly animated film. On 5th January,1914, a little guy called Chaplin joined the Mack Sennett studio, and the pathetic and brilliant character was an instant hit. On 1st July 1919, he started his own first film *The Kid* - with a four year old called Jackie Coogan.

On January 3rd 1929, a chemist called Berthon demonstrated a new colour film process. The film is covered with thousands of microscopic flecks, and is made sensitive by a screening process which filters the three primary colours.

On 3rd February, 1929, MGM put out what was acknowledged as the actual first sound film. It was called: the Broadway Melody. In order to create fluency, the sound engineer Douglas Shearer, pre-recorded music, then played it through loud-speakers on the set for the performers, - so the film could later be married to the recording. Maybe that's enough detail about the early days. It shows, though, the genius and imagination of just a few men, and how this world-wide business found its first legs. I think we all owe a big debt to all those fellas - particularly Mr. Edison.

Georgie Goes A-Wooin'

Mr Cobbleblock was frustrated.

'Tarnation.' he hollered. He really wasn't one for using language of loud expression, but the moment demanded it, in his opinion.

'Alright keeping things in a silent, or controlled mode', he figured, 'but sometimes satisfaction with a word comes only from loudness.'

The reason for his exasperation was Ms Fotheringay. Having reached the dubious age of forty, he'd decided that his singularity was something to be dispensed with; and she was the one chosen for the job. He'd always had a healthy regard for the woman, but it wasn't until he reached this dashed age that he seriously considered making her the one to share his name. So he approached her, and told her of his decision.

Now, Ms F was possibly past the 30 mark, but was still 'acceptable'. Yes , acceptable, to a man of Mr C's charitable disposition. Well, her reaction was not precisely what he'd expected. She laughed loudly. Worse still, she uttered words that were not only less than expected, but were downright hurtful: 'Oh Mr Cobbleblock - you really are a scream.' Then giggling, she moved on. I mean - what was one to do?

Such a thing had jolly-well never happened to him before. To say he was embarrassed, as well as frustrated was probably true. Now, at home in his 'bachelor pad' as some unthinking fellow had called it, he sat down and cogitated on the situation. He could feel another 'tarnation' coming on, but fought against it. 'Control was the thing,' he told himself, 'at all times'.

However, a few words - quite beyond his wishes - did slip out. 'Dratted woman.' Worse still, he had no idea what to do next. He'd made his pitch, if not offer indeed, and had been well and truly rejected. This was indeed a new 'thing' for him.

A new scene, perhaps, in the play of life? Certainly one he'd rather have omitted.

At any rate...onward old boy. He would ring the woman; if the reaction was the same, then that was it? End of scene, so to speak. End of darn play, more like. Thought of discussing it with someone, but thought better of it. People as a rule, find it difficult to keep things to themselves. Didn't want to be the sniggering stock of the whole darn club, after all.

Just then, as he finally moved towards the darn phone, didn't the thing ring. It was her. He could hardly speak for a moment.

"George? It is George, isn't it? This is Dorothy here. Don't mind me ringing, do you?"

"No, course not. Fact is, old thing - I was just about to ring you."

"Oh were you, George? I wonder what you were going to say, hmmm?"

"Well, since you managed to get in first, as they say, then you have the floor, or the air, so to speak."

"Oh well. I suppose so. Thing is, I feel guilty about how I reacted to your offer, if such it was, the other day. It was a tremendous surprise, and one which I fully appreciate. So that is mainly why I'm ringing."

"Mainly, Dorothy?"

"Yes George, mainly. "

"Excuse me, my dear, but that word usually suggests that there is more to come, as it were."

"Now who is being trying? Okay, look I was going to suggest that we meet, formally of course, and talk it all over. What do you think?"

"I'm so glad you said that Dorothy. I was of course going to suggest the same thing. Splendid. One had got-gotten?-the idea that you didn't exactly consider one the most desirable chap in the world. At any rate - meet? Absolutely."

A silence ensues.

"Are you going to suggest a time and place George, - or will we merely talk of meeting."

"Oh yes. I mean no. A place? Let's see - why not that little hotel on the outskirts of town? Rather discreet, I believe. And time? Perhaps I'll leave that one to you, Dorothy. Shared decision, don't you know."

"Well yes - okay. Thing is, I'm frightfully busy at the moment. How about Friday at seven, hmmmm?"

"Absolutely splendid. Friday at seven. See you then."

George poured himself a celebratory drink. The man felt quite elated. He dwelt on the absolute dottiness of life, betimes. There he was, no more than ten minutes ago, and he stricken with remorse. Didn't jolly-well know where to turn. Felt almost rejected.

And now? Now, here he was - like a youngster before his first date. He even went to the phone and kissed it. An instrument of communication indeed.

On passing the mirror, he took a longer glance than usual. What did he see? More importantly, what would she see? A slightly balding man, carrying rather more pounds than were acceptable, - that's what.

What could he do in three days? Choices limited, he feared. Perhaps a visit to town? Could do with improving his wardrobe anyway.? Okay maybe not, but this was a special occasion after all. Well ... potentially. A visit to a good hairdresser? Certainly.

George felt rather good. While he would surely wish that all this damn formality could be skipped over, it was obviously necessary to her. If she actually fancied him, then why not jolly-well get on with it? But if 'wooing' was what the dashed woman wanted, then wooing she shall have.

The time came. He called a taxi, though it was very much against his will. He'd driven all his life to such things, And driven home. This modern pre-occupation with regulatory rules was not to his liking. Not one bit. 'Wouldn't have happened in my father's time' he was fond of saying.

She was there before him. Looked rather fetching too. He observed her from the foyer door, as she fumbled with a hotel brochure. He observed her closely. 'Comes from good stock' was the summing up.

"Dorothy. Good to see you. Not late, I hope? " He kissed her cheek.

"Not at all George. I always like to be early.

"Shall we?' said he, urging her towards the lounge.

They ordered, and relaxed. Like on the phone, there followed a few moments of silence, if not awkwardness. Then they both spoke together.

'Are you nervous George? 'she asked. 'I know I am." Ice-at least-cracked.

'Fact is, Dorothy, I'm not any good at small-talk. Never was. Perhaps I'm a bit of a bore, if truth be told."

"Don't be silly. Of course not. I'm sure we'll get on wonderfully. I like that suit, by the way. Is it new?"

"New? No. Have it a year or two. Don't get much cause to wear it, I suppose.' "Your…ammm…dress looks rather good, if I may say so. Yes indeed. "

"Oh thank you George. You're so kind. I do dress up, occasionally - but seldom buy."

Now that such formalities and accompanying porkies were out of the way, George somehow felt better. "Tell me about yourself, Dorothy." He felt the words slipped out, rather against his wishes, but there they were.

"Gosh, George. How nice of you to ask. What do you want to know, actually?"

"Just trying to make conversation, to be honest. Not wishing to pry. Your family always lived here, have they?"

"Not always - I believe it was about 1740 they moved to Somerset. Rather glad they did, I can tell you. I just love Bath.

As for before that, I fear there's a vagueness lurking. My father's family were of Scottish descent, I believe, with some German connection way back. As for my mother's, English, mostly. London, she said. Not sure she really liked Bath, to be honest."

"Really? The old city-country divide, I suppose. I can understand that. Personally I'd hate to live in London. Great to visit, of course."

"Now, George, I feel I should ask you the same question."

"Well, if you must. Fact is; there's little to tell. My lot, if I may call them that, have always been country-folk, really. Owned lots of land way back, it seems. To do with backing the winning sides, I shouldn't wonder. Now, of course, I've little enough left. Maybe 400 acres, or less. Plus the house of course. According to papers, they date back at least 500 years; a mixture of all-sorts to be honest. Well there had been an 'influx', dare I call it, into our dear old country over the centuries."

" As we have done ourselves, of course."

"Oh absolutely. Infiltrated many a race, I should think - world-wide. A violent history, really."

"Yes…well. History is violence, really. Take the Spanish, Portuguese, French, British, back to the Romans, Greeks, Celts. All travelled and took their armies with them. Strange behaviour, if you ask me. Now here we are, with our 'remnants' you could say. Lucky to have our own little country left, in a way. "

"Excuse me for saying so George, but as one who has benefited from such strange behaviour as you call it, albeit through inheritance, I'm surprised to hear you sounding not altogether appreciative."

"Fair point, Dorothy. Fair point. Truth is, old thing, I was born into this sort of life, and never really had a choice. Sometimes I actually wish I had an ordinary job, with a mortgage, and all that. You could say that one has the choice to do whatever one darn-well wishes; but is that practical, as opposed to theoretical? I doubt it. I'm spoilt, rich and privileged, as you say. As are you, to a certain extent, if I may say so. But are either of us likely to throw it all in and go out to an office or whatever every morning? I think not!"

"A very honest appraisal, I think, George. I'm impressed. "

"Impressed? Are you really? I'm so glad, relieved perhaps. Which brings me to the reason for our meeting, really. Listen, old thing - I really do apologise for my initial behaviour. I really do. Realised later how stupid and ungallant the whole thing must have seemed. Truth is, I'm not exactly versed in the business of 'wooing' - if such a word still exists. And I now sincerely apologise."

" There's no need to George. I suppose I was more amused, really. But to be told out of the blue that you had decided that I was to be 'the one' was, well quite extraordinary, but in a way also charming. But you must agree that the 'other half' in this imaginary arrangement should have at least a little input?"

"Oh absolutely. I quite agree. Unthinking of me. Put it down to lack of education in such things. Quite unforgivable."

"And now here we are, George."

"Here we are indeed. I say how about a refill? Barman? Haven't eaten, I hope? They say there's quite a good restaurant here."

"Really? Well ... I admit I haven't eaten either. Should we have booked, I wonder?"

"Booked? Booked? 'course not. They know me here."

"I see."

"Oh hell. I know, there I go again. Let's just say I'm ready for change. Are you up to the challenge, old thing?"

"Oh I think so, George. I welcome it."

"Cheers."

Inchydoney

Inchydoney:
Where inches become miles; where the strong become donny.
Where walks don't just traverse silky sands, but soft, often soggy, sands, stones, rocks, algae, sand hills, wannabe mountains.
Where even reaching a road means taking on a descent not to be recommended.
Where travellers from ancient lands descend in bucketfuls, and accents pierce the air with strange sounds.
Where clouds dominate a vast sky, allowing the sulky sun mere glimpses of a pale face.

Inchydoney:
Where travelling means experiencing the insides of a special vehicle.
Where its handbrake, last seen on a Fordson tractor in '61, resembles a dangerous weapon
Where passengers are treated to an array of sound, with wind accompaniment.
Where the eye is constantly delighted - wherever it rests.
Where makers of meals are in great competition to tease and please the finicky traveller.
Where Murphy's stout ways, like Barry's tea, leaves opposition floundering.
Where surrounding miles reveal a countryside that aches with new life as its autumnal produce reaches a ripeness to gladden even a Cork farmer.
Where short drives can throw up villages of substance and towns of promise.
Where local accents turn words into song.
Where a son becomes a friend.

Mater

She was 'a woman's woman'
in today's parlance.
Unflattered by the world's
refusal to advance.

She ran her life serenely,
setting agendas to relate.
Knowing there was a time to do
and a time to delegate.

Hers was not a life of leisure,
though enjoyment had its place.
Her love of life and family
we could all appreciate.

Now, in tranquil moments,
when her spirit does surround.
I re-visit special memories
that she left hanging all around.

Pater

Mike would smoke his pipe of peace,
while 'he' would ramble on.
Neighbours, easy friendliness
in a world that's long gone.

I might observe from background,
setting memories in cement.
Kicking heels, and slowly coughing,
looking for acknowledgement.

They would talk of cows and horses;
and the potatoes: 'have you sprayed?'
Of bluestone and washing soda,
and the perfect mixture made.

'He' might shake his walking stick
at cattle in the field;
Saying: 'the fair last week was lousy'
and 'the cows are giving bad yield'.

They were happy in their moaning,
knowing both understood
That it was this communicating
separated men from mud.

Menus

It's selfish, really.
Don't like shellfish, me.

Know what ya mean
It's only a cod really.

Now that's better - that I can get me teeth into.
Better in batter, ya could say.

Thing about selfish is that they never tink about anyone else.
Think that because of their tastes, like, they're superior.

Bit like salmon rushdie .
But at least he can write.

Or maybe Johnny Fish.
Well no, neutral, really.

So selfish is out, ha? how about steak, then?
Well, that might be a mis-steak, if ya know what I mean.

Ah-ha. You know yer onions, wha?
Not mush-room for mis-takes in your head, ha?

But what about youse?
What d'you like?

Since I started talking about u-no-hu being
selfish, I just think that maybe fish isn't the best choice.
How about an egg, with the shell taken off - served on a saucer.
Janey, an egg? An' dats it?
Small appetite, me. You?
Me? Think I'll be bleedin' selfish an' have a rasher!

Jimjam Jody on the Road to There ...

He was roaming along at a steady pace. He didn't care where, just some other place.

His partner neat, and pretty too; she sure looked cool and she acted so.

The jalopy chugged and rolled along; there was no small hurry, and the time was long.

He put on Petty and she just smiled; just the right sound maybe for the coming miles.

She sang and she danced around her chair; just then he realised they were some pair.

To be free in this world was a blessed thing, and to be happy in love really played that thing.

Petty purred and he grimaced with a special voice, and the miles just added like there was no choice. Countryside looked good to their four eyes; when in love you're a sucker to any prize.

As the States changed name and the colours too, they just changed accents ... all sez 'how'er yu?'

People change and ponder their petrified lives, but they do all know it's good to be alive.

You can see the hurt and the happy too, if it's possible to help, then good for you.

So Jane and Jody continued the miles, continued the love and the sometime smiles.

The journey grew good, and the words grew long, but their ain't no finish to an old love song.

Moments

There have been a lot of things that have made me happy over 71 years.

I expect there have been a lot of things that have made me unhappy too; and a lot of people would most likely expect me to write of those, knowing my cussed nature. But no, not this time.

Only two days ago I was fortunate to listen to a programme on a singer called Tibaldi. I'd never heard of her before, which isn't too surprising, as my knowledge of such singers never really went past Callas and Murphy. But the sheer beauty of this voice made me sit up. I believe it was stuff from Tosca that really caught my attention. Or rather, her treatment of it.

For me, I admit, it was a rare moment. While I do always have music on while busy at writing, or fixing something, it is seldom that I feel compelled to stop everything and just listen.

There never was music in my youth. At least, not regularly. My sister could play the piano, and I wish I'd learned too. It is an instrument that delights my untrained ear, whether it is good old Jim Doherty, or that supreme jazz artist Oscar Peterson. But in spite of my early lack of practical experience, there has been a continual appreciation of music in general right through my adult life.

Another moment that also stands out for me was that almost breath-taking time when the one and only Sinatra walked out quietly on the stage in Lansdowne Road in '77. Such "almost greats" as Liza Minnelli and Sammy Davis had been on; but, while I appreciated them both, I felt at the time that their performances were akin to what could be heard any weekend in any of our music cabarets of the time.

Not so yer man. While he was around 74, he took on songs that he could have been forgiven for skipping. Like: the

Soliloquy from *Carousel*, *Where or When*, *Come Rain or Come Shine*, *The Best is Yet to Come*, etc. It is probably incredible that I can even now remember what he sang, which proves the effect of his performance, I suppose. But it is that moment, that delicious awe-inspiring feeling of disbelief, that the most amazing man of song, possibly ever, was there, right in front of our eyes, and doing his thing, for the first and only time in Ireland.

Of course there were others, in that vein. Like the wonderful Ella, when she performed in - was it the Carlton? Twice, in the early 60's. And the almost over-the-hill Dizzy Gillespie in the Concert Hall. I remember again when he walked out first on the stage, and looking at the imposing building just put up his hands and said: 'My ancestral home!' Then he blew that trumpet, and delighted his audience for hours.

Duke Ellington, too, was a pleasure to see, in the Concert Hall. But he, too, was a little the worse for years. Danny Kaye came to The Royal around that time - maybe twice. Maybe some wouldn't put him in the realms of the greats, but his versatility was unusual. And he sure was popular. One night, so many had turned up too late, and couldn't get in. Including me. He opened his upstairs window and sang to us outside. I think many remember that moment.

Were there great Irish moments? Of course - many. But not in music. Okay, The Chieftains in full swing are something to behold. Rory Gallagher was probably the greatest in his line of song.

Rock, at its best, is probably where my heart resides, and it is sad to me that I've never seen the greats from this defining sound. Even that precocious and unbelievably talented mixture called Lynott. Should have- he was around enough. But I was wandering then.

Which brings me to a different kind of enjoyment - sport. A big word, sport. As I grow and slowly evaporate, the word seems to be acquiring a less than wholesome personality. I hate that. Undeserved. It is what defines us, I believe.

When they threw that spear, sunk a knife in that running rabbit, hit that ribald rebel with a perfectly executed left hook, or strangled that uncooperative tiger before it secured a less than perfect breakfast... then it was what was not done only for survival, that was sport too, in a way.

While it has taken us many millennia to really appreciate the value of the damn thing, and the necessity of competition, maybe thanks to the Greeks, we have finally got around to organising it. Now, while homo sapiens have the benefit of the best technology ever available just waiting to be used to stretch the limits of our abilities - what do we do? We cheat. The appearance of dirty lucre has shown up our limitations, maybe.

I would like to see today's hotshots try to play with the kind of clubs that were used 40 years ago, in golf and in tennis. Then we'd see just how good they really are ... or aren't.

Watching athletics this week, I thought of how the pole-vaulters used have a stick that was rigid; whereas the new ones, it seems to me, means you just have to hold on to them, and they propel you over.

Anyway - moments in sport? More a case of memories of special players, doing extraordinary things. Like Mike Gibson managing to always outshine those around him, with his sporting brain, and downright natural ability. Like seeing Christy Ring always do the unexpected. Must have been impossible to mark. Like Mick O'Connell showing such grace and class in every game. Or Cass Clay lift an ordinary sport into something graceful and classy. Enough of that, maybe.

Anyone for the Last '38 Show?

How to record a life? That is my quandary.

To put into words all the happenings, accidents, incidents, calamities, collaborations, successes, failures, and wonderful memories of someone who has lived over seventy years on this never-still orb called Earth. To record accurately what the World was at, at such a time; and how it affected our 'hero'.

It all starts in 1938. 30th October to be exact. It is a significant date for two reasons: our 'hero' was born on that night; and a certain gentleman called Orson Welles chose the same date to broadcast live a programme on American radio called *The War of the Worlds*. It warned the population that the country was being invaded by Aliens. The significance of that warning, vis-a-vis the subsequent behaviour of 'yer man' over the following lifetime had best be quietly ignored. While there is no doubt that some of his behaviour may be alien to a lot of people, and even serve to alienate a lot of people at different times, I think the tale will verify my own belief that he is wholly innocent of all, or most, accoutrements of guilt.

Enough of all that. I will now hand you over to the man himself. After all he knows the story better than me. Before the War I arrived. Aye. Before Adolf and the boys started their marching across other peoples land, causing well-told harm and destruction. Doesn't it seem a long time ago?

Here I am now in the 21st Century, and attempting to recall in accurate detail, the World and life of that long ago.

My own father was born in 1891. He was a nineteenth century man. Maybe that is what brought me to the belief that each century is no more than the length of a passing thought; and each life a mere flurry of wind across the heedless earth. Each generation comes along, with outrageous expectation and a shared disrespect for the poor unfortunates that went before.

Changes occur, certainly. Lifestyles differ, and expectations soar. But I maintain that what really changes is the available technology, and the tools we use to get ourselves through this extraordinary thing called 'life'.

Ultimately, the human being of today has the same fears, hopes, vulnerabilities and capabilities as our forefathers. Or so it seems to me. I know it sounds like the ranting of someone who refuses to give credence to the march of development; someone who would like to think that people like their father, or grand-father, were no different to the high-fliers of today. Look, give a few quid to someone, and it doesn't alter the faults and insecurities he had before he got rich.

All this is like a precursor to all that's to come. So you've been warned.

It is surely a fact that we've no control over where we are born; or who our parents are. Not only that, but our make-up is largely predetermined by who our parents are. We are born with the brains of one, and the nose of another; the build of one, and the temper of another. And so on. So much for the 'individual'. Alright, so we develop in our own little way, and become narky or nice, difficult or deadly, intelligent (sort of), or slightly retarded. And-inevitably, 'not a bit like his parents, God 'elp 'im'.

But that could be as a result of an almighty effort by the poor creature to carve a niche for himself that was going to be 'different'. Not many achieve this high ideal. In my case, I was happy with both where I was born, and with my parents. The 'when' I had some disagreement with; but looking back now, I'm really glad about it. From the safety of seventy plus years, I can say that it was a time that was a wonderful experience to live through.

I and people of my generation were the last to see and taste and sup at the altar of the old Ireland. The land of horses and bicycles; of two-batteried radios and no TV; of black suits and peak caps; of rosary beads and 'bless-me-fathers'; of short pants and canvas shoes; of thre'penny seats and Roy Rogers; of Mrs. Dale's *Diary and Sunday Night Play*; of 'do what you're told,' and a puck on the ear; of porridge for breakfast or a duck egg; of making your own entertainment and 'where the hell have you been?' and of foxtrots and 'diddle-me-arm'. A time when talk of civil war and division still hung in the air, like dew on the grass.

So, a different world indeed. But it was the one chosen for my entrance, and who am I to question the decisions of the Almighty? It seems almost customary to recall and record thoughts from our lives, once we reach past that clinging episode called 'middle age'. It will usually be a process that brings on a smile and a wistful look, at least on the face of the recorder. But, I aim to avoid such obvious tales of 'good old days'; and tell instead some short stories, showing the darker sides of life in those days; and a truer picture, perhaps, of how some of us behaved in our youth.

I was a little divil - officially. A rebel with plenty causes, before young Jimmy Deane got out of short trousers. When I was only seven, I was playing on the front street, and noticed, unfortunately for her, my sister inside the window and making ugly faces at me. What did I do? Without thinking for a moment I picked up a big stone and fired it at the window, smashing it and getting rid of 'that face'. Oh, I paid for my impulsiveness alright, but I didn't care.

Around that time too, or maybe a year or two later, I went over through the fields to where my brother was working. He was about four years older than me. I said something to him that must have been slightly insulting, because he took after me with a vengeance. Luckily, I had the sense to get a head start on him possibly foreseeing his reaction, and the chase was underway. It was at least a mile and a half before I reached the environs of home. I caught sight of a bigger brother, and sought sanctuary. He only laughed, and said 'I'd better hide.' I went up stone steps to a loft, and saw that my possible assailant was on my heels, and foaming from the mouth. He followed me up, and I knew that something desperate was called for to avoid possible death. There was a small window in the loft, and down from it was the roof of a small shed. I jumped onto that, and from there onto the ground - a considerable distance. As I gathered my by now battered body, I looked up and saw that he was not prepared to take the same risk. Escape was procured. I don't think I've ever been so scared ever since!

We had a pony and a small cart with rubber wheels. It was used mainly for delivering milk to the town. One day, I decided that we should knock some fun out of this vehicle, and I got two friends and my little tomboy of a sister to come for a spin. I drove to the top of a hill, in a field and then turned the steed around. With red-indian style whoops and flailing whip, we started down that hill at full speed. Well what followed was something that would put Ben Hur to shame. One of the lads fell out of the cart, my sister was screaming like a crazed banshee, and the poor pony was going at a speed twice that which he'd ever gone before. Then the inevitable happened: the pony fell, the cart capsized, and we were all thrown every which way. When I came too, I surveyed the battle-field; little sis was bawling her little head off and bleeding from both knees; one of the lads had broken his leg; and the other had enough bruises to forestall any immediate jokes. I was badly shaken, and sore as be-damned. The poor pony was quietly having a nervous break-down. When we released him from the harness, he took off at a speed, planned to remove him forever from such a gathering of fools. The repercussions from that episode were long and arduous.

We used fight with our fists a lot then. I think it was a general pastime and indeed, in many ways, a good thing. It got rid of frustrations, and didn't involve any knives or guns. Afterwards, both assailants would be friends again. Great fun. I really do think it was a very honest way to settle disputes; and should have been continued. The travellers still carry on the proud tradition, I'm glad to see.

Anyway, when at National School, between five and twelve, this was very much in vogue. Between classes, there were three ways in which to pass the time: play a bit of football (usually a small sponge ball was all that was available), throw lumps of dirty clay at each other (not in any non-descript way, though - we'd have two teams and lay into the enemy with vigour); and the third way was to have a good old decent fight with someone. While I always favoured the first, it usually led to me partaking in the last. For football was always a sport that led the participants to get over exuberant, and still is, obviously. So, when someone's shoulder got where it shouldn't have, or when the other team got a goal, or when everything wasn't completely as you wanted it, what would you do? Hit someone, of course. It brought instant gratification, and instant retaliation. Now, while I was certainly very much in favour of this offshoot of sport and a frequent participant, I have to admit that I wasn't particularly good at it. I could land the odd punch certainly, and even the odd knock-out being a strong and wiry youngster; but when I came up against someone with a bit of finesse and quicker hands, I was liable to feel a helluva lot more punches than I would land.

This came to a head one day when I had this 'grudge' match. Me and this chap didn't really like each other, shall we say. Well, he was certainly getting the better of me, and I was very much the worse for wear. So I thought drastic action is called for, and fast. So I hit him in the neck, and hard. He almost choked. I realised much later that he could have done, but right then all I knew is that I had won. The teacher was called in, his parents were called in, the doctor was called in - but no, I did not call my parents in. The lad recovered, and it was all forgotten - eventually . I don't think we ever talked again though.

There were many more such memories, of course - like how I would let the air out of the teacher's tyres whenever she hit me, or burst the tyre if it was really sore. But enough for now, I think. They are not exactly earth- shattering revelations, I know. They wouldn't compare to hearing that say- Dan O'Donnell had been heard to use a swear word; or that Mary O'Hara had once played in a rock band, or Bertie Ahearn had once taught diction lessons, or that Charlie Haughey had been 'born again'.

It was a raw, and rough and tumble time, I guess. I submit it was a more honest way of life, though. People were not two-faced, and not prepared to criticise behind backs; and the violence of then was relatively harmless. I am only recalling some of my own experiences here, and would like to hear others recall theirs, so I could compare.

Moseying Through the Deserts of My Mind

By the lapping waters
of Portmarnock's velvet
strand, I walked in tune
with nature - all alone.

As I strolled in blissful
ignorance of the World's
festering woes, I recalled
in solitude, my fleeing life.

All the great and good
and harmful events that
form a day; and the piling
on of days into my time.

Soon, I sat and gazed in
wonder at the beauty that
lay there; that was always
there, under oblivious eyes.

The lapwing, the wader
and the bobbing seagull, too,
seem to say: this is the
natural thing to do.

Nearby dunes, ever-changing,
hold their secrets in the sands;
bent grass gelling billions
of grains into a dune.

I watch the near horizon,
beckoning to me to explore.
but I am too earth-bound
and contented, in the now.

Mr. Whimsy Takes A Stroll

There was little happening in the village of Here-an-there most weekends.

First up would be Tom Wurzell; he could be seen any morning, wandering about at his daily chores. One of his first tasks would be to water the weeds down at the village green. He liked weeds, see. Most agreed that, yes weeds could indeed be quite colourful, and should be encouraged.

Next to appear would probably be Jenny Jones. Before most folk had raised a thought, ne'er mind a head, she would be on her way to the Chapel. Dressed in her best flowery hat, and swaying party dress, she'd be swanning her way down the street even before Tom had completed his first weed-in. A song, words of which had withered somewhat in the wailing past, would nevertheless flow forth; as a trail of bonhomie would follow Jenny, as she set about preparing things for the coming cleric.

So, it was a quiet place. Seldom would a loud word be uttered, as each one went about their quaint and exquisite lives. Indeed, the daily utterances from said cleric had a regularity that seemed set in clay, as the assembly nodded and smiled, thankful for the surety of sameness; not sure what the man was saying precisely, but knowing that it was familiar and un-provoking.

Sometimes there might alight a stranger in this haven of civility. One such was Hughie Grenoble. Came from afar had Hughie. Wandered in after weeks on the road, his bicycle looking the worse for use. As he unbuckled his clips and put them in the pockets of his loose trousers, he looked around and liked what he saw. He observed the studied movements of the gentlefolk of Here-an-there; also the strangely colourful appearance of the place. 'At last,' he thought, he'd found a place worthy of his favour. He parked his beloved bike at the font, in the green. Indeed, so taken was he with the thoughtful provision of a watering hole, that he proceeded to take off his shirt, and his hobnails, and started his ablutions there and then. How good the water felt as he splattered it around; his somewhat wasted vest receiving a fair share, as did his aerated socks.

But eyes were busy. Many eyes were busy with the taking in of such uncouth behaviour on their beloved green. Mutterings were reaching a murmur as the collected angst of a conservative population aah-ed and ooh-ed in unison, reaching a righteous crescendo as yet another item was seen to leave the environs of Hughie's vast body. Finally, it cooled somewhat as he was seen to attempt to dry himself - the tail of shirt being handy. Mayhap there was a tinge of disappointment in some, as such high jinks and high excitement were alien indeed to their much-starved palate. But Hughie was not to grace them with his presence for long.

While looking for the ideal in lodgings, he came across Miss Have-alot. She, prim suppresser of all things pertaining to excitement, had been impressed reservedly by the exquisite performance of this stranger, and wondered if perhaps he might have the wherewithal to remove her from her suffocating nature, and finally release her true, erotic self. Hughie though, had other ideas. Much as he appreciated a challenge, he had too much on his plate just then to go head-long into an occasion of vain-glorious sin.

Twice in his thirty year bicycling had he been ushered up an aisle, and twice had he bicycled away from such tyings-down. So his available circle of activity was curtailed by the necessity of avoidance. Not that he wouldn't be made welcome in this village. Barely audible mutterings made him feel that he would indeed be the ideal partner for the said Miss Have-alot. To be fair and honest, he was tempted. He liked the smell of the place. Was impressed, too, by the unusual behaviour of the inhabitants as they moved and acted in a way he found 'interesting'.

'I could fit in here,' he thought - once. But he was fair ruined by a life spent on the highway, finding it hard to accept any form of 'normality'. So with the sobbing Miss Have-alot tugging at his shoulder, Hughie once more mounted his bike, and shot into his uncertain future.

Here-an-there only slowly recovered from his visit. One Sunday the cleric was heard to almost shout some inaudible annoyance, almost waking his faithful throng from their reveries.

Old John Sackville decided there had to be more to the world than his known patch, and purchased a fine new bicycle. With a packed haversack on his back, the three-man brass band lending a final hurrah to his epic journey, and the whole population in tears, John the intrepid explorer was on his way. Being new to the intricacies of this un-motorised vehicle, his departure was somewhat wobbly, but depart he did.

Three full days he was absent. Three days of dreadful hardship, as he heroically investigated the frightening realities of foreign climes. When he did return, collapsing theatrically in the village square with Tom Wurzell administering the first rights with his trusty watering can, he found that his future was secured as he continually related his unbelievable tales to a wondered audience.

'Aye,' he mused betimes, 'there is a lot to be said for the sameness of Here-an-there.'

No one liked to interfere too much in other people's lives. There might be a kind word offered now and then, by way of advice, if someone asked. Like when Tom mentioned once that he felt lonely, betimes. It was just a casual mention, really. But word did get around, and the common feeling was that perhaps he should get a companion.

There was a lot of sympathy for Tom in the village. About forty plus, he'd never hurt anyone's feelings, and attended to his chores without fail. A companion, they said. He clearly heard the word 'partner' mentioned, at least once; but he wasn't quite sure what a partner was? Ms Feversham once mentioned the word 'wife'. A wife? It really did sound far too extreme a measure altogether. No a 'companion' had just about the right ring to it, he decided. But where to get one?

Being a man of limited means, and doubtful experience, he decided to place an ad. The local population fair sat up and took notice when reading: 'Companion wanted. Must be young, hard-working, and with independent means. Contact Box Number 6542.'

Of course it had to be Tom, they decided. He, and they, waited on replies. The editor had promised to send on any to his house - if there were any replies.

The postman passed his door each day. Tom bothered; had he been too short with his ad.? Maybe he should have put in a photograph? 'Perhaps not,' he thought as he passed the mirror, settling his hair with a spit.

Finally, a reply. It was from a Miss Trepidorous from about 20 miles away. The letter said that she read the advert, and took a while to reply as she was quite shy. She too required a companion, she said, and maybe they should meet? Perhaps you would phone me?'

Phone? Phone? Tom had never any call to use a phone. But there it was. Then there was a knock on the door. It was a neighbour, Robert. The right man - how fortuitous. They went to find a public phone, and Robert did the ringing, handing over the handset on hearing an answer. Tom started talking into the ear-piece. Soon, though, he heard the sweet sound of a friendly female voice come tumbling into his ear. He talked, he mumbled, he scrambled through some sort of chat; not knowing what he was saying.

"Will you come here? Or will I go to Here-an-there?"

"You'll go there," shouted Robert.

"Four o clock. Meet her under the clock. Tomorrow." He repeated the agreement.

She hung up. Tom travelled alone. His poor mind was troubled. What would she look like? Would she be young? Or poor? He found the clock and waited.

After a while a young girl stood near. 'That must be her.' he figured. 'By gum - she's young and good looking.' Went to move towards her when a young bloke came and took her away.

Tom was flabbergasted, or something. He was going to shout after him: 'Hey. That's mine.' But he didn't. Waited more. And waited. Felt worse then. After all his sweatin', all his preparin' - she weren't even going to turn up. By gum.'

He went to move away, in disgust. Spotted an elderly lady nearby, looking and smiling at him. 'What's wrong with her? he wondered. Moved on. Then she called his name. Swirled around. "Tom. I knew it was you. " They shook hands. "You mean you're ... ? But you're ... " he was stuck for words. "What am I, Tom?" she teased. "Old? Is that the word you want?"

"No - No. 'Course not. This is a bad start, isn't it? I'm sorry. Thought you weren't coming, see."

"Oh. Was I late? Never noticed." She was still teasing him, he felt. Tried to remember her name; then it came ... Gertrude. "Do you want a drink ... amm ... Gertrude?"

"Of course. lead on."

So they became an item' in Here-an-there. It was the consensus that they were 'well met'. She sold her little cottage, and moved into Tom's abode. She charmed the locals, and made poor, staid Tom Wurzell the happiest man in the whole place. He changed in other ways, too. Dressed better, became more confident, and would be sometimes seen to smile while walking, and uttering a loud 'By Gum.'

So, things continued to move along in their leisurely way. The seasons came and went; folk offered help where needed, and it was generally agreed that there couldn't be a better place to live in the whole wide world.

This is a story of old times. Or is it of modern times? For it concerns a place near to my heart that in a way transcends time. You will gather from the tone of the telling that I feel close to it, and all it represents. I intend to represent those involved in a compassionate way, really; but also, I hope, in way commensurate with the way I remember them all. For, believe me, I remember it all. As they say ... I was there.

I'm reluctant to put a time to it; or a place. Yes ... of course we have the name of the village - my beloved Here-an-there ... .but it's geographical location? No chance. Let's just say that it is a part of old England that represents, for me at least, all that is beautiful and irreplaceable in our make-up. The different characters if you want to look on them in such a way, as characters in a play, or story-are direct representations of people I knew and loved - very dearly.

Maybe you might say dear reader, presuming you do exist; that I am merely trying to make profit out of the lives of friends? Please do not think so. This place, this village is very dear to my heart. I merely wish to represent those very special people in my own amateur way. If I seem to concentrate too much on the actual happenings of their day-to-day carry-on's, maybe it is my way of portraying, in a practical way, their real character.

By the way, let's admit - we'd all like to live there.

Positioning

Giles Thornbury had come to Here-an-there while still a child. Parents appeared to have taken to the name of the place, and promptly decided to uproot and move. Luckily for them, and indeed for Giles, they were in a position to do so, having relatively substantial means, gained in the gleeful days of the Empire. The family having been not only loyal, but also aware of the importance of positioning.

So, when they dutifully passed away, their only son was fully appreciative of their legacy. His sister Suzanne was a few years younger, and had been eventually persuaded to move herself and her beloved Jonathan rather far away. Of course he loved his sister, loved her dearly, but he considered the close proximity of family to be potentially detrimental to his plans. One was eternally in danger of becoming enmeshed in the dreaded domestics, not to mention the parochial.

Not that Giles had any specific plans. Indeed, 'long-term' was not really in keeping with the man's nature. 'To enjoy oneself to the full' was as far as he had extended his thinking on the subject. It seemed to him to be sufficient unto the day; after all, one could not easily see into the future, where he was led to believe that all sorts of un-niceties lurked.

He liked his home town. Though he had travelled a lot, and explored the best that the World outside had to offer, he still was satisfied to return. Yes, e'enthough those blessed years of dissipation and amorous complexity may have committed lesser men to continuation, Giles was aware of his duty. After all, a lot is expected of one, when put in the area of privilege.

Now, at the relatively advanced age of 42, he decided that it was time to procure a partner. Father, and indeed mother, were loathe to bring up the subject; but, from time to time, it did rear it's not quite ugly head. Once, when dear sister broached the subject, she had added rather brusquely, he thought that the lady chosen would certainly expect a certain standard, and that perhaps some lessons in the business of wooing may not be detrimental. The sheer cheek of the woman. The business of wooing indeed.

He organised a party. Well, he mentioned it to his housekeeper, and she organised it. An absolute necessity, was Mrs Jenkins. She had been with the family for a long time, and had stayed on thankfully, when parents departed. He thought it was doubtful that she would, as she had surely let it be known that she was not entirely in favour of his life-style. Giles had watched this careful consideration of their personal world from a short distance, without intrusion. That she had stayed on was somewhat of a victory, in his opinion; though Suzanne had expressed reservations about life after her departure. Damn woman.

Plans were drawn up. Giles supplied the list of guests, though there were a few names that Mrs Jenkins was decidedly unhappy about. The evening arrived. And so did the guests. He had settled on an eclectic mix of friends of the family, and people from the village. Inevitably, that meant Lords of the Realm, and those from a lesser heritage. Would it work? He really didn't know.

Lord Arundel accompanied by someone who was decidedly different and definitely younger than his last escort, was first to arrive. He brushed by Giles, with a wave of dispersal, avoiding the necessity of introduction. Making for the vicinity of 'drinkies', he finally relaxed.

Very soon, everybody seemed to come together. Familiar faces were prevalent, to Mrs Jenkin's obvious delight. Soon, everyone was sat down, and relaxed.

But where to position himself had been a particular problem to Giles? He had specifically invited Rosemary Atkens, who he knew rather well, though not in the way he would wish to.

A handsome lady indeed, who had rather good connections. But to sit beside her straight away, would be churlish, surely? He spent some time seeing to people, drink-wise, and chatting. After all, that was part of his job so to speak. Eventually, he caught the eye of Mrs Jenkins Or rather, she caught his.

"I've seen to it that there is a spare seat right beside Miss Huckleberry." she informed him, while winking .

"Miss Huckle ... " he almost shouted in exasperation. A perfectly nice lady, but hardly what he had in mind. Then, having looked in her direction, the said lady waved to him. He now had no option left. He took his seat, to the audible titter of those around. To make things even more uncomfortable, Rosemary Atkins was seated across the table. She was smiling, demurely.

" It's such a fine place you have here, Mr. Thornbury," said Miss H.

"Oh please call me Giles. And thank you. I do like it, I must admit; though to inherit is far more pleasurable that purchasing, don't you think?"

"Fact is, I wouldn't know Giles. My name is Agatha, by the way. Strange that we haven't met - formally up to now, isn't it?"

"I can assure you, Agatha, that Giles is not one for formalities," said Rosemary. "Likes to get to the bottom of things straight away, I'd say."

"Thank you, Rosemary, for the kind words…if such they be. But I can assure you that your assumptions are merely conjecture."

" Oh come, come Giles, old boy," said Lord Arundel rather loudly, as he sat far away. "I can assure you all that our host is not only popular with the females around this country, preferring to spread his qualities in far distant beds, but also nearer to home, or so they say."

Giles was flabbergasted. After all, this was his house, his party. The words so far were not complimentary, and if he didn't take care of it, he feared the onset of loss. Reparation was called for.

"My dear lord, I thank you for those complimentary words. I only wish that they were true. The fact is that my life has been nothing more than that of a lonely bachelor who seeks solace in the company of those who are kind enough to offer such. And by the way, one can't help noticing that you, dear friend, have the enviable knack of having company that varies between young, available and less so on both counts. Perhaps some tips may come my way before the evening's out."

The party settled down, and good humour filled the air. Mrs Jenkins plus her two helpers, taken on for the evening, quite excelled themselves. Food pleased, and wine flowed generously. Afterwards, people mingled. Tom Wurzell and his Gertrude at first found the whole thing mesmerising, being unused to such company, and indeed, such surroundings. But a word from Fred Garter put them at ease.

While accepting, not for the first time, another refill, Fred said to Tom: "Listen here to me, Tom Wurzell. Thee is as good as anyone 'ere, right? And don't you forget that. You and your good lady mix and mingle and let it be seen that while some may consider themselves a touch above thee and I . . well we damn well do not. Right?"

And so it went. In fact, Giles himself made a point of spending some time with that same three, and that alone relaxed all. Although Tom's remark to Giles about how well' Ms Arkins looked, did leave the poor man feeling that some definite move was called for. One problem was the continuing close proximity of Miss Huckleberry. While he did find himself getting to actually quite like the woman, he found it hard to shake off his original plan, if such it was. Though

Rosemary's rather churlish comment at table didn't fully endear her to him.

When Agatha intimated she would perhaps enjoy the experience of gliding across the floor, poor Giles was stricken with guilt, "But of course, my dear. How perfectly neglectful of me. Please do me the honour."

Their dancing was intermingled with glancing. Mostly from Giles. 'How interesting, ' he noted at some particular pairing. But Agatha was no quitter. Her conversation ensured that his mind stayed attuned to her, and her alone. She admitted to herself that while she found the man to be somewhat of a flirt, she nonetheless became more interested than she initially thought possible. After all, she was a woman of independent means, and of very independent mind. For some time, she had discarded the thought of any man sharing her life. One or two unfortunate romances in her earlier life had quite turned her off; and at forty she was resigned to a life where she would be in complete control.

But this was cooking up into a challenge. On the one hand there was the almost exciting challenge of 'besting' Miss Atkins, whom she always found to be not to her liking. Far too confident of her own abilities entirely for Agatha's liking. As far as Agatha was concerned, she herself could be, with just a little effort, damn well as fine as the next, as long as there was sufficient reason to appear so. Was there now reason? That indeed was the question.

This man called Giles Thornbury, while surely 'a good catch' as her mother used say far too often for Agatha's liking, was still unfortunate enough to be not only a mere man, but also one with the word 'bed' attached to his mind every time he even talked to a female under fifty. The challenges mounted. The dance finished.

''What now?' thought Agatha. She made for her table, comprised of a friend (female) and two members of family.

They smiled adorably, and said nothing. Giles thanked her profusely, perhaps a tad too much, and said that he hoped they could repeat the experience later. He moved off. Her friend, Emily, touched her hand and asked, pointedly: 'Well?'

"Please Emily. Don't ask."

"I see."

"What ? What do you mean 'you see.' No you don't see."

Brother Richard took a more philosophical line. "The trouble with idealism I often find, is that it leaves a trail of reality in its wake."

"For a brother you really can be an awful ass."

Agatha was already feeling quite frustrated, and didn't need people's sarcastic comments at that moment. The table became quiet, and in danger of conversation steeping to the level of the urbane. Just then, Leticia Pettigrew passed by, and stopped to have a word. "Oh hello, Agatha. Glad to meet you again. Isn't it absolutely splendid?"

"Leticia? How nice to see you. Yes. It is quite an evening, isn't it? Tell me : "how have you been? And how is life on one's own?"

"It seems to me, Agatha, that you are the one that should be the expert in that field. But never fear. They say Giles is quite taken with you." With that, she moved on. Agatha fumed. Agatha fumed ... and fumed.

Meanwhile, the male members of this gathering seemed to somehow cluster. Lord Arundel assumed the mantle of elder statesman, gathering the supposedly less important mortals in one's circle. Giles felt decidedly uncomfortable in this manufactured circle, and tended to act as host and master. That alone created a problem, insofar as some, like Tom and Fred, found themselves in the middle of a dilemma. On the one hand, there was the lord, who both saw as a bit of a bore, but on the other hand, he was a bloody lord, and they were both expected to bow to the situation. Then there was Mr. Thornbury.

"Tis a fine building you live in, - am - Giles," said Fred to he, nervously.

"Yes. Interesting that you should call it a 'building', Fred. I see what you mean, though. To be honest, if I was in a position where I had to go out and buy, I do believe I would go for a rather old house. One with thick stone walls, and small windows. You know the type."

"I know the type, alright, ...but if you don't mind me saying so .. I doubt that you're the type. Horses for courses, like." Wurzell sniggered.

"Well 'pon my soul. Not sure just how one should take that comment, Fred. Still, I'll be forgiving and presume that no hurt was intended. It might surprise you to know that I really would settle into such a house. At least I believe I would."

"Maybe it would come down to who you were sharing it with, Mr. Thornbury?" This from Gertrude, who was feeling relaxed now, and able to express herself.

"No doubt you are right, Gertrude. Which brings one back to matter in hand, I fear."

"There's a house, 200 years old, about a mile down the road. They say they want to sell and get movin'," said Fred. "'Tis a fine place I think, with a thatch roof."

"Is it indeed?" asked Giles. "By jove. Thatch is a fine English tradition, you know; though they say the Irish actually started it. Is it a cottage would you say, Fred?"

"Oh aye."

"Many of our great artists lived in old cottages, you know." said Gertrude.

"Absolutely, Gertrude. I'm glad to hear you show an interest. In fact one of my favourites, William Blake, used live not awfully far away from here."

"Felpham, Mr Thornbury?"

"Felpham. Absolutely. Are you a fan of his too, perchance?"

"But of course. Even us peasants sometimes rise to poetry and art now and then ya know."

"Touché, old girl. Bravo. I say, Tom, that's quite a girl you got there, you know."

"Oh aye," said Tom, with a hint of bewilderment in his voice. He looked at his Gertrude with a questioning, but admiring, look.

"And what about Wordsworth, then eh?" asked Fred, "Wasn't it Dove Cottage he called 'is place?"

"Dove Cottage."

Poor Giles was getting quite excited at this stage, with the extent of knowledge that surrounded him. "Isn't it in the Lake District?"

"Aye." said Gertrude. " It used to be called the 'The Dove and Olive Bough'. It's been looked after, they say, and by the way it was Dorothy Wordsworth what called it: 'truly and literally a cottage', and they paid ten pounds a year for it."

"I say. How absolutely wonderful. What do you all say to this suggestion I wonder? We all go and visit this cottage, that and the whole damn Lake District as well. "

"I think that would be wonderful, Mr…am.….Giles. Of course, if everyone would agree?" Gertrude said, looking around.

"I think it depends on who's usin' 'em … and on what they be, really." Tom seemed to be off on one his solo runs again.

"Tom, love; whatever is thee saying?" Gertrude was both perplexed and anxious.

"Well, I was trying to work out what words are worth, that's all."

"And with that bit of glorious philosophy, I shall leave thee. I really enjoyed our chat, and I thank you all. As for this tour, etc. I shall get back to you about it. Now please go and help yourselves to refills, wont you? "

Fred and Tom led the rush. Meanwhile, the lord and his cohorts were taking up a separate corner. The conversation seemed to be more downbeat, more run-of-the-mill, it appeared to Giles, as he approached, still recovering from his recent education. It was interesting that, while the sexes separated, so also did the classes.

"Oh there you are, Giles." said the good lord, loudly. "I was afraid you were ensconced in the environments of the milieu. However, you dear friend, may be able to release us all from this delirium. My friend on the right, whom you may know as Siegfried Montague, was saying that the reality of living in such a place as Here-an-there is that one is absolutely cut-off from where the fun and frolics is happening, in effect - London. I wonder what your feelings are on this subject, old boy?"

Giles felt he was being manipulated. And if so, it was for the vilification of the surrounding support. So, care was called for.

"My lord," said he, assuming an air of gravitas. "Who better than you knows too well that, while one may with impunity indulge in the hell-holes of our beloved Capital city, here at home there is the opportunity of similar sereptidude, with very similar results. Without the same expense, I should add - not that mere money would ever come into it for such as you, dear friend."

The air was filled with laughter, and indeed, clapping. Giles took the applause with aplomb. He even took the opportunity to bow to the audience. The winning of the first round was always important in his opinion; and winning it on home turf was darn-well a must.

The evening became even more jolly, and blessedly better mixed. Giles felt that the time for positive action was at hand. Rosemary hovered. Miss Huckleberry smiled a mite too broadly, perhaps harbouring some feeling of victory.

'There are victories ... and victories.' was Giles' feeling.

That woman Leticia seemed a little larger than life personality-wise. While he knew only vaguely of her history, Giles really thought of her as more of a danger, than a challenge. After all, to summarily disperse one husband to the wilds of Scotland would possibly leave her with the belief that dispensability was part of the game. Giles was a man who believed that marriage was to be one of absolute fairness, where each shared responsibility. To do so with such as she seemed an unlikely prospect.

He stopped and had another glass of wine with Fred and co. Tom made the observation that it was the best night-out he'd ever had.

"'Tom, my friend. I'm so delighted to hear it. And you're all so welcome. Now you made the comment earlier on that such and such a lady looked rather good to you ... excusing your presence, Gertrude. Now I am going to put upon you this decision. Okay, not quite a decision, but a mere observation, perhaps. I am in a quandary, you see. No doubt you are all too well aware of its content, if not its outcome. One feels under pressure to acquire a partner. Pardon the expression, but I am loathe to use the word 'wife' for the moment. Being a man of means, I am therefore in a different position, to shall we say most. No hurt intended, I assure you. But we have come to a hiatus, it seems to me. Decisions are called for, and the wrong one could be quite catastrophic I feel. So I have come to you, dear friends, to assist me in my hour of need.

"Eh, a small advert in paper did the job for me-am-Giles. Just thee look at what I got." This from Tom, pointing to Gertrude.

"No good asking me" said Fred. "I had some run-ins with the females in me day, but I escaped, see."

"Most amusing, I'm sure." said Giles, "but it does seem that you are both missing the point. I am now here and so are they. No need for me to put in an advert as you say, Tom. And while you may feel fortunate in your escape, Fred, it could be that I do not wish to share your good fortune. No, the situation is coming to a head, dear friends, and one is bothered with indecision."

"If I could say a few words here," said Gertrude, gathering her skirt around her amplitude; "Thee has maybe three fine women out there, and all of 'em chokin' to get hold of you. Maybe thy few sheckles has a little to do with their ardour? Though there's no doubt that your personals has also attracted them, if I may say so. Now, what to do? Miss Atkins seems to me most suited to your means, if I could put it that way. A fine big lady of ample means, they say. But is she to your liking? Could you manage her strong and independent inclinations? Would she drive thee round the bend with her superior ways? Then there's Miss Huckleberry. How to describe her? Thee and she seemed to be the perfect couple on floor, if I may say so. How pleasing she seems, at least to me. They say her family used be well-off, and fell on 'ard times. That 'appens. It comes down to your feelings for her, I suppose. Which leaves our friend Leticia. Eh, I don't know what to make of her, and that's a fact. A woman of character Giles, that's for sure. They say that she kicked her poor Scottish husband out of bed and out of mind. I don't know just what kind of man he was, I really don't. But I know what kind of man you are Giles Thornbury, least I think as how I do. If thee likes a challenge, one that lasts all thy life, then you know where to go. Forgive me for bein' so forward, Sir - but thee asked."

"I did indeed. And I thank you for your candour. Most illuminating, if I may say so. Now, I suppose, I must take up that cudgel, and fight the good fight, as they say. "

With that, Giles moved on. As the night progressed, the party became louder. The wine, supplemented with much spirit, had the inevitable effect of leading some to a more raucous behaviour than they would usually indulge in. Especially those that unwisely mixed the two. Giles worried that things could get a mite out of hand, thereby ruining all that had proceeded.

It was then fate interfered. Miss Huckleberry decided to help matters along, in a manner of speaking. Seeing Miss Atkins as her most dangerous adversary, a-la Giles that is, she took the good woman aside, and hit her with a sucker punch, so to speak.

"Miss Atkins. I do believe you and our host have become quite good friends. Though it is not quite my business, I feel I should at least make you aware of the situation as I see it. While I admit to having had shall we say, a rather distant interest in the gentleman at one stage, it rather quickly disappeared when I found out exactly what he is made of. Naturally, I checked out everything. During his sojourn in London, it seems he had more than one affair with men. Yes, yes - I know. That is his business, and of little lasting interest to you. Except it appears his diminution has once again reared it's curly head. Okay, he is well known to have a flattering effect on the odd female, and I suppose one would appear a bit churlish if not admitting to finding the gentleman positively charming betimes. But it is my belief, Miss Atkins, that once a smattering of interest is bestowed on the same sex, then that is where ones interest tends to reside. Now, as I say, it is only because I felt it my duty to tell you this because to me, you have always seemed a most gracious lady, and I'd hate to see anyone enter the fray as they say, without a complete knowledge of what one was entering into. Forgive me if I offend you in any way."

Miss Atkins looked like someone who had been hit by a torrent of words. It had the same effect as being overcome by an unwelcome reality. How to respond? How to react? How to-indeed-hit back? While she never had any great opinions of Miss Huckleberry, good or bad, the woman did at least seem quite sober, and genuine. But why did she come out with such startling news? If news it be. She admitted to being reasonably interested in the said Giles, but, if this were true, where lies her future interest now? Should she confront the gentleman and demand some answers? Maybe so, but certainly not here. Not now. This was his big night, and one should not be ungrateful for such a lavish bestowal of equanimity. No. The time will come; the moment will show itself when it is ready.

She turned, and simply said: "Thank you, Miss Huckleberry. While I do not question your 'news' if such it be, I shall surely check up on its veracity, and take suitable windings. In the meantime, why don't we meander, and see what the evening offers?"

And so it went. Miss Huckleberry left with a smile that would not go away; and Miss Atkins tended to sidle towards the sidelines, looking with a different slant on the developing situation.

Leticia had been keeping a low profile. It was not her way; but she considered the situation needed delicate handling, to put it mildly. Since her return to home, she'd managed to complete her (their)divorce, and admitted to liking the feeling of being 'free'. This party business, and the seeming challenge ahead, vis-à-vis Giles and all that entailed, had put a slight interest into her humdrum life. Though she seldom admitted to missing London, and her life there, there was, nevertheless something missing. Perhaps the Nursing? - she asked herself that question, at odd times. But no. Not really her, she decided. 'Doing good' and looking after people for a living was all very well, but it was basically an occupation for other people'. No. What was missing was someone in her life. Could the said Giles possibly be the one? Quite a question. If she decided the answer was 'Yes' - then so it would be.

Yes, there were other participants, but nothing she couldn't handle. As for Giles? Not exactly her kind, of course - but the chap could be tamed. Oh yes, there was a definite challenge available here if she so desired.

She spotted him talking to 'those people' Tom and Fred again. Goodness knows why. 'The challenges mount.' she smiled.

Miss Hertinshaw was actually dancing with the good lord. Miss Atkins was apparently in some kind of a huff, and Miss Huckleberry was involved with others in a drinking session.

'How strange people can be, sometimes.' she mused. 'They can act out of character at the drop of a hat. Well - so can I.'

She approached Giles and dragged him towards the dance floor. Poor chap had no decision in the matter. She thought of actually leading him in the dance, but thought better of it. Instead she smiled and chatted and soon had the man eating out of her hand, as they say.

The thought: 'what an inferior animal they are?' - was never too far from Leticia's mind.

When dance was over, he asked if perhaps she'd like a drink? 'But of course,' was the swift answer.

Giles was well aware of glancing eyes. Felt guilty, but also enchanted. Things had happened so quickly, that he found himself simply accepting the situation, and relaxing. This Leticia woman was so hard to figure out though. On the other hand, she was possibly the best-looking lady in the place, and most agreeable. At least, betimes. He caught Gertrude's eye as she passed, and she actually winked at him, and smiled. Seemed like an approval.

One or two were seen to get their coats, and amble towards the door. There was a feeling of things reaching an end. Or was the final act still to take place? He rather thought so. Leticia seemed to be making sure he devoted his time to her, and only her. Manipulation? He rather hoped not. But on the other hand, the consternation and confusion of a mere half-hour ago did seem to be dissipating somewhat, and that had to be a good thing surely?

Tom and Fred waved to him from afar. The Lord seemed to be exiting quietly, for a change. Giles relaxed and ordered two more drinks. Any future Act in this rather captivating play he really looked forward to.

Meanwhile, Tom, Fred and Gertrude had also got themselves into a 'situation'. There happened to be a lady called Cecilia Poppinshaw in the cast, I mean the gathering, and she took a determined interest in the said Fred. Now, our Fred was not particularly interested in the persuance of character; indeed he had little interest in the normally fascinating game of chess. But Cecilia had. To her, the choosing, and laying of a possible partner was very much a game of chess, and boy was she determined to land her choice. For choice it was.

Having spent some valuable time surveying the possible candidates for her game, she fixed on the in some ways doubtful Fred. Okay he may be past his most virile years, and may even have a history that could have done with more devotion to the wilder side of life, but hey. Time could settle all that, eh? She herself had possibly an alternate history. To her, the throwing away of a once-off youth on some singular male seemed a step quite too far. Even if he happened to be suitably suitable in most ways, she would certainly rue the absence of days and nights of wonder spent in some tent or castle, in the arms of some Sheikh, or cheque-happy Count.

And now? Well, now there was reality. Now there was the coming of wrinkles, the coming of an age of a different wonder. Now there was Fred. Or was there?

As for the other two, well, Gertrude was feeling motherly. For a woman of her age, this was not a feeling she really wanted. She and Tom had settled on the possibility of spending their left years alone. Alone with each other, that is. When Gertrude mentioned the question of children, Tom positively blew a fuse. For he was really not into diversity. While he was very pleased with his sonorous selection of Gertrude, and her addition to his world; the thought of adding another to his diminished circle was unquestionably out of the question.

The very nerve of the woman - a child? A squealing, squabbling being, designed to upset the most set of humanity. What was the woman thinking?

Gertrude, for her part, being imbued with sufficient wiles to deal with a mere male in high dudgeon, quietly smiled. Besides, this was not the time for intimate, or inanimate discussion with her Tom. She and only she, would choose the battle-ground.

About then, Cecilia was providing more than adequate distraction, and not only for Fred. While he was busy running, nay hiding, from this intrusion on his perfectly-formed bachelorhood, she was seen tripping the farm of another man. Hugh Muskey, a man of 42 years, though fifty if a day, according to Fred , was a latecomer to the party.

He and Fred, shall we say, knew each other. First there was the question of an unpaid bill. Hugh had claimed that some items had not been properly attended to, and to pay up until all was right would be, well wrong. Of course Fred was never happy when his workmanship was questioned, and so this monetary disagreement drove stakes of hate between the two, and a definite dislikeability grew.

Hugh farmed a modest holding in the hinterlands of Here-an-there, and was happy with his lot. At least within the constraints of a farmers mind not given to talk of contentment and such.

Enter Cecilia. When she spotted the incoming Hugh at one end, and the outgoing Fred at the other, a plan formed. Deviousness had its place when desperation plundered the mind. She, a woman with a propensity for paint and powder and flouncing dress, was difficult to miss. Difficult to ignore.

If Hugh was targeted ... then Hugh was struck. If not completely by choice, he still found himself handing the good woman a large G&T; and when he noticed those noticing him he wasn't half chuffed. Not used to notoriety, him.

Then he noticed Fred. At first, he noticed her noticing Fred. A lot. Having quickly worked out the mathematical formula of $2 + 2$, his arm soon found itself around her shoulder, and a surreptitious glance towards Fred said, loudly: 'Eh, thy oily mechanic; thee has no chance.'

Giles, meanwhile, was busy being busy circling the crowd, circling the problem. He found it infinitely interesting how far people would go to create diversity, and fun. Of course, he knew that most of his own life had a sincere devotion to such. But time was being obstinately belligerent, and was forcing him to change. There was however, one rather delicious distraction earlier. It involved he and the suddenly interesting concubine of the good lord. She had indicated to him an interest in 'upstairs'. That look in her eye was quite unmistakable to Giles, having seen it before in the throes of battle, shall we say. Separately they ascended. Without too many words or fuss, had what is commonly known in less refined circles as a 'quickie' (as with all such cheap expressions, though - demonstrably accurate, but painfully inadequate, in Giles' opinion). On descending, they both returned to their developing chaos.

Leticia was threatening to leave, seemingly in rather a huff. Giles found it difficult to keep tabs on what was happening all around him, so he repaired to the only one he could think of who he felt may have her finger on the respective pulse, so to speak - the redoubtable Gertrude.

" I say Gertrude; sorry for impinging on you again, old thing, but can you tell me what is going on? Is Leticia leaving? And why? It can't possibly involve me ... can it?"

"Certainly not, Mr Hertinshaw. Of course, I can only guess at what is happening at the moment, but if I circulate around for a while, I may be able to mix and gather the odd comments, and so on; and then be able to come back to you with a better picture Sir."

"Oh I say; would you really? I'd be most heartily grateful to you. And by the way, I detest that additive Sir; especially from a friend."

She departed; he turned to Fred and Tom. "Do you know - I envy you two."

"Eeh. Thee don't know the 'alf of it." said Fred, ruefully.

"Oh? Not trouble in paradise, I hope?"

"Paradise can be a murky place betimes," said Fred.

"Whatever's the matter, then?"

"See that woman over there talking to that rapscallion Hugh Maskey?"

"Yes. Isn't that.. em? What of her?"

"She been annoying me all day, she has. I made it clear I did, I didn't want nothin' to do with her, see? Happy enough, me. - with what I've got, like; happy man, me."

"Yes ... .and?" Giles was by now feeling quite perplexed. "I mean, if the good lady has transferred her affections elsewhere, doesn't that rather solve your problem. Or have I missed something?"

"Thee has," said Tom trying to hold back his merriment.

Fred's look suggested that merriment was far from his mind. "I take it thee's not familiar with yon Maskey, then? Accused me of not doing a prop."

Martyr

I am the eternal writer,
Lurking in the shadows of success;
Languishing in anonymity,
Clinging in the Sunderlands of 1st div.

I'm the Everton supporter,
The 'bad news' reporter;
The independent voter
With the one litre motor.

I'm the 'Ireland's alright' man
'If you don't give a shite, man'.
I'm the GAA guerrier
With the rosary and worrier.

Nobody heard me sing the
Ballad of the unknown writer.
Nobody knows the number
Of 'Nos' that dropped in my doors.

Writing is my bind,
Ever straining my mind;
Ever trying to amend,
Weaving words to the end.

Destiny
(April 27th 1994)

A painful birth,
but a birth, for all that.
Into the Nations of the Earth
comes a new and colourful member.

Strange sight, indeed,
on a Durban morning.
A flag, to represent all
is raised in triumph.

Strange deeds, indeed,
all over this ancient land.
Non-whites dare to vote
and influence their destiny.

The undying spirit,
of a ravaged people,
has overcome prejudice
and pitiable ignorance.

The lion is, indeed, uncaged.
Let us rejoice, and wish them well.
Equality for all is a desirable dream;
Let's hope time will fulfil theirs.

The Invisibles.

One can tire of being talked of
in so many different ways.
So important - but anonymous,
never ceases to amaze.

They speak of 'ordinary people'
with a superior sort of spiel.
Thing is, those that prattle on
don't seem extraordinary to me.

Then, God help us, there's the elderly
and all the problems in our lives.
And, to rub it in, cheap holidays
for the over fifty-fives.

Just in case I might forget it,
I'm one of the unemployed.
The experts will soon remind me
to make sure I stay annoyed.

Of course I'm 'socially excluded'
when I thought I was feeling fine.
And case I wonder where I am?
I'm just 'under the bread line'.

So, how could I feel lonely, when
a member of so many clubs?
But it would be nice to have a name,
and to afford to visit pubs.

Romance ... in the Stone

"Such romantic countryside,"
she sighed through the window
of her hired car;
stopping only to look.

Hearing her, the farmer
Sighed. 'Sure lady,' he thought,
'there's romance there, if
you can afford it'.

Watching the retreating chariot,
he spat out the thought.
'Is there romance in this
grinding life of mine, eh?'

'Maybe it's in these rocks?
Or in those fields with their three
inches of soil? Or in those
nettles that will not die?'

He thought of his two sons
in far-off lands; 'I hope ye find
ye're romance, for there's
nought for ye here'.

Putting on his coat, he carried
the scythe on his shoulder, and walked
wearily home. 'Aye,' he said,
'Romance how are ya?' and spat again.

Rambling

Got a 12 hour train journey to Dublin in '50 with my mother. Came to stay in '58. Boat to Paddy's Graveyard in '65. Back here in '70.

From Enniscrone to Manor Street; from Dublin to Holyhead. From Cornwall to Somerset; from Bath to Newquay, to Penzance, to Reading, to Oxford, to Birmingham. From there to Coventry, to Co. Down, to Enniskillen, to Dublin.

Circles; always the circles. Always on the move. Job sent me to Waterford, Galway, Sligo, Cork, Limerick.

I knew all the roads long before bypass was heard of. When the word landlady meant a fry soaked in grease for dinner, and a bed of nails. When a fancy car was a Ford Prefect, and potholes were part of every road. When a pint was a few bob, and wages fourteen quid a week. When Mrs Dale had her diary opened every day for all to read; and such as Jimmy Deane was still crying to Mamma to have his nappy changed.

I started working at six, and never stopped when at home. Maybe a quid a week from me brother. I worked with horses, donkeys, dogs and brothers. Binders, scythes, clippers, ploughs; made silage with a buck-rake, and made hay whenever I could. Spread flax on the side of a hill, and helped transport it to Derry mills. Helped sort hundreds of tons of spuds for export to Spain; spent weeks on knees weeding, sowing, picking planting - all sorts. Worked days and nights on a combine harvester; and cut turf for the winter fuel while kept home from school. Helped supply milk to the village (twice a day).

Did 'ship to shore' exam in Lesson Park; went to night-school in Reading and Oxford to learn all about telecommunications. Was charge-hand in new exchanges; and offered job of being in charge of all Midland Contracts with BT. I turned it down.

Was in a group in Coventry in '68, and given five gigs in Derby. Then sent to Northern Ireland - overnight.

Evidence

Have you ever seen the sun slip
red-faced, behind the sea?
Or a flock of happy swallows fly
regimental, in a V?

Have you heard the sound of children,
all playful, on a swing?
Or the sight and sound of blackbirds,
all manic, on the wing?

There's a time in early morning,
on a beach or quiet bay;
when a stillness, over-powering,
introduces a new day.

If we look real closely,
we can see life in a stone.
There's consolation in the knowing
that we're not quite alone.

Exit Right ...

The roar of the greasepaint
The smell of the crowd
The distance between us
Your silence so loud

Our sharing of moments
When ions apart
The appearance of passion
'mid shattering hearts

Your thespian prowess
Away from the stage
Brings roars of approval
All within your head.

All life's contradictions
Are laid at our door
So I'll raise up the curtain
As I exit once more.

Equal Opposites

Twelve thousand years
in this fair land since
the male first dared
to lift his hand

To slap and tame
the female bum
and dominate their
rattle and hum.

From caveman bold
To computer nerd
They controlled and beat
Half of the herd

But things were stirrin'
In the bridget store
One dared to speak
And shout 'no more'

Too soon they all
Did raise a scare
Resist the Toms
Just wouldn't dare

Agreement came
To fight no more
More fun to make
More love, less war

So with equal pay
And equal lay
They now can smile
On way to clay

Indecision Time

I see no early crocus
Portraying future lightening
In the greyness of this
February morn

No witty words of wisdom
Dancing in the confines
Of the frozen imagination
Of my mind

There's little consolation
In unsuitable scribblings
That pour onto the page
Without conviction

Should I suffer on
And graft away the morning
Without the consolation of one
Smile-making line

Or let it be and cast away
This unproductive pencil
And seek sweet inspiration
Elsewhere

Roving

'How can the poem and the stink and the grating noise, the quality of light, the tone, the habit and the dream, be set down alive?

When you collect marine animals there are certain flat worms so delicate that they are almost impossible to capture whole, for they break and shrivel under the touch. You must let them ooze and crawl of their own will onto a knife blade, and then lift them gently into a jar of water.

And perhaps that might be the way to write this book? to open the page and to let the stories crawl in?' For I ain't no goddamn wordsmith. I ain't fitted with no brain that at will can call up the right words, and set them down like they were set there by some Steinbeck, or Miller.

The world I've lived through up to now has been one that was splattered with allsorts. I ain't sayin' I can capture them and put them into no neat story, all gift-wrapped for yon reader to open up and enjoy. All I got is the memory of them; the goods and the bads; all their wily ways, and all their plenty goodness.

For a life is just that, to me. Moving through a part of earth where you're surrounded most times by a mixture of people who intrude on your dailies. Sometimes you may be alone a while; alone and contemplatin'. That's alright too. Sometimes all elated; and other times all down in the pits. Most often maybe somewhere in between. Those people you come in contact with, maybe many thousand afore you're finished, are gonna leave their mark in some ways. Just like you leave your little mark on them.

Now, like I said, it sure ain't no easy task to have all this set down alive. But I aim to try. And if yon reader is gonna find betimes that people and stories and confusions have seemed to just crawl in by themselves - why that's because I done left page open, see?

In times when maybe folk like Fionn Mac Cool and his like were big cheeses around here, there was this story of a very large pig coming in from the sea down County Sligo ways, and terrorising the place. He was black and ugly. Eventually they managed to kill this intruder, and buried it where it fell. A large mound was built around it, and stories abounded, especially after it's death. Good career move, as they say.

The area acquired a new name then , in Gaelic, of course - Muckduff. Just a small area, where small farms were the norm. Maybe a lot of the farmers were large and strong, but their holdings were never more than one hundred acres; maybe mostly around forty or so.

Townlands acquired their own names then: like Carriccarden, Carrowhubbock, and other such fierce-sounding concoctions. The nearest village was Enniscrone-or Inis Eascraic Abhann - 'the isle on the fishy river.' It is blessed with a beach that must extend to three miles and more. Many's the beautiful, and less so, damsel strolled those golden sands with parasol and dreams.

The fact of a nearby golf course, inter-twined around those same hills, would in the early days take the fancy of those who considered themselves above the average yokel; and they would mix with their own, telling tales of imaginary holes-in-one. Later, to their chagrin, life took a turn or two for the worse, and their sacred world was invaded by the dreaded yokels. Their future was in doubt.

'What's next to go?' they wondered. 'Hunting? Plus Fours? Private lounge?'

The recently departed visitors would certainly never have stood for it. But in '38, that dratted future was way ahead. Indeed, so far ahead that the drums of war were pounding, with their familiar and almost reassuring sound. The said visitors were making conciliatory sounds, and wondering if perhaps we might lend a hand with the emerging little problem?

Some did, maybe out of boredom, but generally we said: 'thanks for asking, old chap, but maybe not this time.' The Irish world indeed, was still in the grip of stagnation.

It was into such a world that I then stepped. On 30th October, Mr Welles announced to the listening public that we were being invaded by Aliens. I could never really forgive that large and talented genius for such an act. But, alien or not, I'd landed.

A large family surrounded, and two more followed, to make our crowded house ... worse. But once I got things figured… after about a year and a half…sure it wasn't too bad at all.

I had time then to survey and study my surroundings. Up to then sure I was like a darned doll, which had bottles and what-nots stuck into me gob; and wasn't allowed to even pee like a normal hobo. When I got the hang of the walkin' crack though, sure I was away and running. Mostly, it wasn't as bad as I'd thought, and several things, including people had to be re-assessed. Several times maybe. I saw later, when one of the opposition dropped in and stayed, that the thing called a cot was not for me at all, like it got to be but a bloody box. It was beside a big fire a lot of the time, and a fire that sparked, at that. Seen big lads coming in with somethin' called turf all the time and throwin' it on.

Boy - but I gathered a great familiarity with darned turf later on. Outside of my box home were big stones.

Was it 'flags' they calls 'em? Once one of those big bucks put me on those darned flags, and sure I nearly died - the cold of it. There was a kinda loft in front of me - but high up - and I could see a few of them climbing a step thing to go up there at night. Every night. At least, any time I was awake to see 'em.

I was glad when I got the hang of the talkin'. I could give back at least a little of the bloody gab I'd been struck with all those years when all I could communicate with was the sound of me lungs, and they stretched. Sure mostly they didn't even take notice of me at all. I'd decided that that time was at an end, though.

Talkin' and walkin' would empower me, and revenge would be mine. I think I got big fierce quick. Sure it was great. To see the outside for the first time was a revelation ... or somethin'. I'd thought there wasn't an outside, really; not so much of it, anyway. Sure the sky alone was massive. And then there was the animals. A cow looked like somethin' I'd never thought was possible. But when I saw a pig and a horse, not to mention a bloody ass, sure I wondered what next?

Oh I knew about dogs alright. There was always the dog. Was it 'Hearty' it was called? Hated it. By God but it was a big yoke. Thing is it always seemed to get more food than I did. Once it finished a load of stuff and came over and licked me face. Begod, I could have done somethin' bad to that dog if I was bigger.

Strange thing about all the big bucks around, and them with the dresses, was that they started to be nice to me. Hard to figure, like, but I thought I might as well let them at it. I wasn't one to make decisions about all on a Sunday, like; and if it meant getting sweets and all sorts, even when I didn't want them, was okay for the minute.

Mostly, I decided that this life they'd dropped me into , without asking mind, had the opportunity to make it work to my advantage.

Then I found meself at five. I can tell you now that things can change damn quick if you're not looking. There I was and in control of my growing life and they sends me off to school. I'd heard of it of course. Them that was older and they talking sometimes like they knew so much that there seemed no need for such as teachers and all them that kept telling you allsorts. Boy was I to find out differently. Sure they started telling me so many things that I wondered what the hell I'd been doing all my troubled life? Had anyone told me that two and two was four? Had they hell!

And then there was the question of words. Words is it? By golly but I learned the use of words. In between the clatter on the ears, and the loud use of unusual words that were new-sounding, and the never-ending song of life that was going on around me; and the clatter on the head, and the giving-out bit. I think I was beginning to learn that my time was either going to be one of fun, or one of suffering.

My surroundings? Like I said early on; nearly ideal. All that beach and stuff. All that confusion. Getting it all down.

Now there's the bitch of a job. But people don't want to be bothered with detail. Sure people is detailed up to their oxters with their own lives. Every minute a detail. If that of another is to be of interest, then it better be put in an interesting way, least that's what I think.

Maybe the forties might seem too long ago entirely for people nowadays, but maybe if iotas can be gleaned out of the murk of it, and pinned down nicely, then a smile might even assimilate on reading. I'll try that tack. Maybe a day in the life, sort of thing?

My father was the sort of man who thought that if there is adequate help available on own doorstep, then there shouldn't be need for any from outside. He was a natural at delegation. As for his own life? He was born in 1891, only a few miles away. A big cheese in the IRA; commander or something of North Mayo Division (we were near Mayo border). His uncle was left this farm on outskirts of Enniscrone, but he went off to the States, and informed Dad that he could have the bloody place if he wanted it, as he himself wasn't coming back. He took it; no better man. He was on his way.

Married Frances Caffrey from few miles away. Often felt I was blessed indeed to have such a mother. That was '21. The house was, is, a very old farmhouse: slated roof, one storey, few rooms. Thick walls and small windows. Comfortable. Cold, but comfortable. You grew up hardy in those days.

My day started with work, and continued that way - from early.

Dad ran a farm that was different to the norm. It was geared to production. To just give a clue: we supplied milk to half the town; this entailed carrying quarts and pints, and half pints, to customers on way to school. Also meant helping with the milking very early; scouring buckets, or gathering in cows - maybe at 7 o'clock. Later got a grand pony and cart with rubber wheels and put large enamel container in back, with tap. That continued for another 40 plus years.

My Mum started it all about '30. It was the kind of job had to be got out of the way before the real work began. And it was an everyday thing.

My brother was a butcher and remained one for 51 years. We supplied him with the meat, and that too meant a lotta work. Raised plenty of sheep, cattle and pigs. Killed and prepared them too. In the early days cattle tied up to wall with halter, and felled with a big sledge . . well to keep away from flailing hooves until he dead. Sheep got knife in throat and blood drained. And so on. Pigs too; then thrown into big barrel of boiling water, to take hairs off. They knew how to scream. Of course there was also plenty fowl around - of all kinds. Seen a turkey killed with a shovel - just cut neck off.

Mum got boxes of day old chicks every Xmas. Also plenty veg grown - of all kind. Self sufficient? Near enough. Used go out with a .22 rifle evenings, brother would have shot gun, to get rabbits. Helped the menu.

We grew wheat, oats, barley, flax, beet, turnips, peas, potatoes, and so on. All physical work in those days. I'd be on knees in field, with bits of jute bag on knees, for long days. Kept home from school a lot. Planting, picking, weeding, sowing, sorting. A never-ending circus - but no one was laughing.

We exported seed potatoes to Spain; sent flax to Derry. All this meant work continued thru winter. So it goes.

Any break from this at all? Sure. We made our own fun. The nearby sand-hills were handy; make a sleigh and slide down; the ice on the wee lakes in winter meant sliding and falling; slipping and laughing. Far side of the hills was the beach. Cool water. There was a cinema. Best was always the serials; continued every Friday. But also we were molly-coddled by the reassuring presence of such as Lash Larue; Roy Rogers; Hopalong Cassidy; while such as Bette Davis, or Gene Tierney reminded us young brats that out there somewhere were lassies that didn't really look too like the home grown variety. Marilyn set the bar too high entirely.

Football after school - soccer mostly, as the Rovers were a big deal. Fishing? Sometimes, but it never really got hold of me. Main trouble was that any dallying on way home meant that the boss would be ever so little annoyed if slave didn't turn up in time. So moments had to be stolen, and appreciated.

To show the differ of the forties from later is difficult. Maybe it wasn't much so. People wore suits and ties. Even farmers in the fields often had ties. Dark the pervading colour. Just like today. Dark the pervading mood, indeed.

The neighbours would gather and sombre tones would reign. They gathered a lot. Talking was a pastime favoured. Our house was always open it seemed. All houses, maybe. And the old pair would stop and sit. Hours of yapping. And tea.

Talk of war, and politics. Of people and animals. Of prices and ... - 'will ya get out of here and sweep the yard, gasúr.' Little sign of progress. Little industry, if any. Little machinery, if any. The scythe still used, if not the sickle sometimes. Horse-drawn binder being talked about.

The horse was the thing, though. Had to have at least two. Most had a donkey too. Useful yoke, that - tough and willing. Maybe a car might alight in the town; maybe two. A lift would be a treat. One was a taxi. Was it called something else?

Dad eventually got an old Ford. He gave me, much later, one of the shortest of driving lessons in history. We were on the farm, and he told me to 'get in, and try not to hit any of the cattle.' That was it, and I got a licence for a quid or two. As long as I replaced it every three years, I never had to have an official test. I suppose I came in handy betimes when he mightn't feel fully happy with driving home. He sure was a popular man. Up to his death in '67, he'd be also in demand by people to fix up pensions - IRA ones no doubt - or such; or to fill in forms etc. He was a County Council member for many years, earlier.

Yeah open pages -what's dropping in next?

The usual day? The usual was work, for such as me. But for the townies it was eternal searching for diversion. Because our place was near, they might stroll up, betimes. Not to offer for work, but to find fun. If they found from me that such as threshing was on; or some such, they sure would come in plenty. Can't remember where they might have got hold of hurley-sticks then, but they would bring such, and similars; trying to catch rats and mice out of stacks of corn, and send them crashing through the air. Inventing fun came easy to those boys. Of course they thought I'd great times. The truth could hurt.

Fighting was popular then. With fists, I mean. All the time. Killed drudgery, maybe. At school it was a favourite. That and throwing lumps of wet clay at each other; and football - probably a small rubber ball. A few times we, someone, organised a fight between top of town and bottom. There was a hill in middle. It was hectic. Like in old westerns where everyone just joins in. Nobody knew or cared who won. Difference between us and westerns was that we would actually hit ... and hard. Now if any of those ever-so-tough cowpokes ever got a puck in the mouth, they'd a go runnin' to their mammies. Interesting that I found in '58 and up to about '61, it was popular in Dublin too. I'd a few scuffles, I can tell. Stoneybatter was in the process of civilisation, I fear; and on the road to the dratted respectability.

But I wander, pilgrim. Mind betimes does that. Truth to tell I'd not gotten past the age of 12 or 13 when I'm sent off again. Boarding school. Wont dwell too much on it, though. Five years of learnin' and five years of sufferin', you could say. Fun too; lots of sports that I loved, and could play good as the next. Lots of drudgery; fighting; being hit-again-by teachers - a lot. Worst maybe was the darn regimentation. Up to 7o'c Mass; study; break; classes; break; classes; more classes; football - if you wanted to or not; study; bed at about 10. Wash in cold water; starve after meals; steal Bishop's apples; over walls to shops -to get survival food. If caught - big troubles.

Yeah - that was learnin'. For me.

Likes? Truth is, I was good at English and Irish. Even told so by teacher - an amazing happening then. Why did it take me near 40 years to put it into some kind of practice? Now I can go to Rome and see some of the places that came through the Latin classes ... somehow. That's taken me just 50 years. Greece Athens will be a held-onto treat.

Of course all of my holidays meant back to normal duty - only more so (including any-odd-weekend). But time was moving on. Or was it? Not noticeably. My friends and their families were leaving. Just leaving. Ireland was a desperate place, in many ways. Sisters were gone too. To nursing mostly. At least in Britain they got paid while training.

Of course, I didn't feel too sorry for those who considered themselves old enough to behave in as if in control of their lives. Dancing was big. My oldest brother even gave dancing lessons, at dances. Ballroom was king. Old Victor Sylvester used bring over his enormous gang of wind-blowers to my Aunt's dance-hall, and that was considered such a big event. I might be given the honour of polishing the shoes of some budding Astaire - more likely a budding Cooper, with limited words and missing steps.

Of course that was earlier. Earlier, before I knew the difference between a quick-step and avoid. Some bloke called Joe Loss would come too; I think we were so underwhelmed by the name that we would go down just to see him arrive? They said he was good.

I liked to see the Irish stuff. Not that I knew the difference, but only that it was ours. There was plenty of it too. A bloke called Mick Del (without the full name applied) was a favourite. Brose Walsh, and so many more. A precursor to the showband era.

In the '60s, so often talked about, there was little sign of the budding evolution, I can promise you. The 4P's were still prospering; the Country Club was strong; The Crystal was still a favourite by us, and if a lift to Bray was somehow available, or even to outside of Naas, it would be unlikely to be turned down. Out of town was out of norm.

Of course I'm-again-running ahead of time. That was early 60's in Dublin. Not a lot of difference. Ireland was Ireland. Is it still? Of course; only some have become enamoured with their imaginary sophistication that considerations have excelled performance. We're a vulnerable race; maybe a vulnerable invention? I think the man or woman in charge had a wonderful sense of humour. Otherwise it would be difficult to understand the allowance of diversification allowed in our so-called development.

Maybe it's time for me to carry you folk out of the darkness. Yeah? Was there a darkness? Not half. Long time our country was in shit street. Our leader even went to London to tell the gentlemen that had left their own country at a time of need that they were deserters. Jaysus. Several times he did it. Pat's Day and the like. Some way of supporting the hardship of those wonderful and hard-working men who couldn't earn a crust at home. Later, when I joined them, I'd talk to some who'd spent their lives over. Sure often I'd find a little bitterness lingering. Some would have attempted a comeback; maybe hope to buy. Sure the place had changed so much that the divils had no chance.

Prices was one thing - out of reach. But the people ? Those that they had carried over in their hearts, and talked fondly of all the years. Changed altogether. They soon find what it was like to be a stranger in your own town; in your own country. 'Moved on' they called it. Moved away. Only way was to return. Dreams is right. No more bloody dreams. Those wonderful, hard-working and honest men who had often kept the home fires burning by their sweat. While I only spent 3 and a half years over myself (plus 2 in the North of),it was enough to get the picture. Betimes, I felt ashamed. Roving, I've been. One last return to base.

I'm between 5 and 12. Short pants and fair hair. Hand-me-down clothes; and a devil-may-care attitude. A bit backward, really. A bit slow. Maybe remedial was what was needed, but sure the word hadn't been invented, never mind treatment. I was a struggler; always struggling through. Should have gone to a technical school, of course; learned a decent trade. Good with my hands always. Could fix things. Still like that. But I'd no say then in where I went. No say. No not feeling sorry or such; no sense at all in that. Just recounting how it was. No more.

So there I was. Used take notice a lot. Found people strange - and wonderful. There was Blackie Dowd and he trudging down towards his forge. Used 'give him a hand' on way home. Gas man . He'd put me on the bellows, sure or holding the horse. Aye - the horse was the thing then. Always loved that animal. Plenty of them then indeed. Busy man.

Snooks Dowd, and he already out fixing his nets. Fishing was big deal. Snorted a lot. Would work in the store in the winters, if fishing out.

George Helly opening his little shop. Sold radios and such. Wet and dry batteries. Fixed bikes too. A lovely man, and unusual in that he had a quick wit, and ready jokes.

Freddie Gannon and he already out sitting on his low wall. Never knew for sure what was his story. Believe he spent most of his time in England. Also unusual because he would give great time to the likes of me. Sure 'big' people had better things to be doing. Not he. A great favourite. A lot of his time would be spent next door, though. Next door where he would find his nemesis.

Micky the Cobbler. They sure would get through a lot of words in a day. Entertainment laid on and free.

John Howley, at the bridge. Another home from the hills. Aye - the hills of far away.

Brother too, though he rarely stayed long. The Master, and he strolling out. Would try to avoid him, mostly. Severe betimes. Only two teachers, then. One, Miss Rouse, for infants. Her and her bike. We'd wonder how such a weak-looking instrument could take such weight. Whenever she'd beat us in the wrong, we'd let the wind out of the tyres. If severe, we'd puncture it.

Me and Christy. Inseparable, us.

Darkie lived in Duck Street then, by the river. Spent his life fishing. Aye, his life on the waves; until that nasty un-giving damn sea took him away. Drowned with two others, and he only no more than 40. His brother and Tommy Forde too. Heard it on the radio one day I was getting lift home from someone; trouble was they never gave names, and didn't find out until home. Dangerous game, surely.

There's Mrs Conway and she opening up her wee shop. A small corner of house, but she managed to fit a lot into it, for sure. Severe glasses she wore, though a smile wasn't that unusual.

Nearer us was another 'Miss' Conway. Now there was a tough wee woman. Maybe 4 foot 10, but hardy as an ass. Her superstitions would guide her life. Her nephew came to work for her, and stayed. He was a bit daft, really. Unpredictable, at least.

All this was at the bottom of the hill. Down-town. Beyond it the square. On the square, a pub at each corner. Good old Mary Rafter had a great old place. A fine lady indeed. The'Shnug' was popular - for some. At one side she kept groceries. Handy when a 'wan' would wander in for a loaf and maybe leave with a wee naggin, if not a skinful.

Eamon Rafter had another - Pilot Bar, with sea-faring lore and memories. He had his name too: Trick.

But the other bar was, is, owned by the Hopkins family. Brother Brian and the one and only Bell. People would go in to her to get insulted. Brian was a one-off, though. He was doing a line with the barmaid across in Mary's for 40 years. He'd make a sign across to her through window, and would then disappear for an hour. Customers would try hard to catch him throwing back a fast shot of whiskey, - but no chance. Fast mover, Brian.

To the left of the square was a road down to the pier. The cliffs were high and dangerous then. Much later supported.

The Marine ballroom, owned then by my Aunt. She and her husband the great Pat O Hara. He of the big band. Was seldom around, he. Sometimes I'd be let in for free to dances - but she'd then put me in charge of the cloak-room. Or maybe into the mineral bar - minerals and tea. Only right too.

Tessie Gildea, and her great shout: 'is it one or two?' The big fella's showing off, pretending to be sophisticated. Couldn't even spell it, and Astaire had little to fear from those low-stepping chancers. The girlíns and their fancy dresses; and hair that was three hours in the fixing. It was a famous - and most popular dance hall, though. The maple floor was said to be the best.

Aunt Teresa was special, though. Good to us, and most likeable.

The next road ,and only other, had a different history. Mostly Council houses, and soon to be empty. Families fleeing the poverty, and seldom to come back. Sad memories: English; Gillespie; Gannon; Gildea; Llewellyn and so on. Warriors all, who deserved better.

Anyway, maybe that's enough. Here I am outside the school, and I'd better go in. Maybe continue this another day. Nice to reminisce, and bring to mind those from near 60 years ago. All part of my growing up, and all special in their own way.

Winning

'Tight lines' is oft the bonded wish
when one attempts to catch a fish.
'Swing well' the golfing guru shouts
when teeing off his new recruit.

When people share an interest
a bond develops in the set.
Competition may suggest a 'line'
but wish is sincere at the time.

Now Bridge folk chat and socialise.
All are friends, and damn the lies.
But when the cards fair hit the deck
no skin and hair are held in check.

On tennis courts white flesh will flash,
while gentle lobs suggest 'no match.'
Then sets are lost and volleys fly.
'Friends no more' the tight-faced cry.

Most sporting folk can so soon see
all signs of human frailty.
One things sure, on this isle of mist,
A 'friendly game' does not exist.

Lucky?

One of the lucky generation,
the over-fifty kind.
An interesting way of looking
at an accident of time.

We were reared on Stan 'n Ollie
in glorious black n white.
The ultimate release valve
no matter what your plight.

Reared too, on steaming porridge,
greens, and other nasty things.
Made to listen to long stories
of turnip-headed kings.

Radio days, and rodeos;
six-guns, saddle and black hat.
Serials on Friday night.
Saturday? - on the mat.

Days of canvas shoes, and no sox;
one-coloured shirts of white.
Of holding hands, and no sex;
and rosary at night.

Oh yes; we had the sixties:
protest, rock & roll and booze.
We thought we had the answers
looking back, I'm not so sure.

JFK was blown away;
Luther King and Bobby too.
Too high a price for freedom
if this legacy is true.

So what have we to hand on
in this generation test?
It appears we weren't lucky;
just confused - like the rest.

Climatic Repercussions in a Country With No Hay

The cold wind bloweth
with Eastern threat.
Naked trees shiver, but
hinder not its progress.

Fire smoke spirals
into angry skies.
Peat and coal mere supplements
in this best and worst of worlds.

'At least it's not raining,'
a bleak and silly salutation.
Our nature nurtures us
against the cold realities.

Yet there is always hope
in home, friends, and certainties.
A welcoming smile can be
heaven, upon this freezing Earth.

Shadows

There was a darkness
across my childhood.
A mere pup in that isle of dogs
licking the scattered bones.

Reared at the deathbed
of an ancient way of life.
Its thoughts, its moods
invaded my very bones.

The un-shared power of the head of house.
Mothers quiet in their certainties.
Children sure of their place; but knowing its uselessness.
There was a rhythm.
Oh yes; the Church promised its destinies.

Age beat its own rhythm.
All-powerful teachers
wagging fingers of priests;
Neighbours, talk of war, and want.

How do you recover?
How do you record?
The trespassers departed; but legacies linger.
I strive towards the light.

The Colourings of Life

Colours, how they
prejudice my life;
providing me
with necessary hue.

The absolute of red;
garishness of green;
the infinity of blue;
stapleness of white.

Variety for all, to suit
each changing mood.
Still, I envy the certainty
of an artist's eye.

I think with an amateur's mind;
see with an amateurs eye.
My appreciation lacks the cohesion of Matisse;
    the glory of Gauguin.
But, I too can see the colours of my life.

Temporary Returns

The New Year had kicked off as Jimbo hit town. He had arranged to meet Jill, but went early just to have a look around, and survey this emerging Ireland that he kept hearing about.

He'd been in Scotland for many years, but came home for the week.

Jill had been a constant in his life, though being away so much left them both in need of some solution. Maybe, if things went well, they could sort things before he went back. That was the 'biggie' for Jimbo. He was happy to work and live in Scotland. Got on so well with them, and the work was good. While he thought, now and again of return, the fact was that the longer he stayed away, the more accustomed he became to being an emigrant.

In his forays South, he'd encountered many who were in the same way of thinking. One problem was, he found years of absence leaves you estranged from family and former friends. Visits home seemed sometimes like you were the visitor, there for a few days. People talked about your life away, and such. Sometimes you even got the feeling they were a bit sorry for you.

Then there were the prices. Thought they were out of control, in a way. How was the likes of he to buy a house here? And family? Sure they all had their own lives now, and there simply was no place for him to stay, if he returned. That was the truth of it.

He walked down O Connell Street, and across Henry Street. A stroll around Moore St was a must, and how he smiled with the memories. Stopped for a pint in Conway's, as he used do, in the 'old days'. Not changed much.

The unusual sun outside seemed to invite him out. Surprised to see so many there before him; and so many youngsters drinking, not to mention so many coloureds on the streets. When he left this town, the only strangers he had ever encountered were Irish. The pint tasted good. Better than in Glasgow, anyway. Checked the time, and got another. When he returned, there was a row started. Seemed to be two youngsters at first, but it soon spread. Jimbo moved to one side, to avoid any trouble.

It was only 12 o'clock on a Saturday, and he was very surprised at amount of alcohol being consumed. Now, he knew Glasgow was no home for saints, and that Saturdays meant footie, and footie meant jar. But this was worse. This was serious stuff. Got his back to a wall, far from the centre of the row. Then a knife appeared. It flashed in the sunlight, reminding him of too many similars across the water. He went to return to inside; they brushed against him, and Jimbo pushed.

Then, he found the knife in his side. The pain was excruciating. He dropped to the ground. Blood was oozing, and he tried to stand-up. By then there was up to twelve involved, and things were getting serious. Made his way inside, and asked the barman to call a taxi. He was in the Mater quickly. The scene inside the A&E was eye-opening. Chaos reigned.

Finally, he got checked-in, and found a seat. Phoned Jill and told her the story. She got so upset, started sobbing. He told her he'd be alright as soon as he got seen, and patched up. She said she was on her way. Made his way to the gents, only to find a fight going on inside; blood on the floor, and language flying. Left.

When Jill arrived, they hugged for ages. She sobbed and sobbed. The nurse finally patched him up, and said the Doctor would see him shortly. A few hours later, he did.

As they made their way out, Jimbo quietly decided that, if this was the new Ireland, they could have it.

The Pier of Enniscrone

How long I looked at it
And at its surrounding beauty.
For youth sees beauty
Where old heads see desolation.
Before me the boats.
Boats that brought me
Fish to accompany a chip.
Boats with men of brawn
And working ethics.
Before me a sea of waves,
A sea of much promise.
Beyond its miles and smiles
Lies a land of more promise -
No certainties, just maybes.
Behind me a village with
Hopes of being a town.
A place of wonder to me.
Wonder why I left it?
Left it and its surrounding.
Neighbours of wondrous name
Carrahubbock; Muckduff;
Frankfort; Carrickgarry.
A place indeed of wondrous
People too; known to me now
By their acquired names:
Snooks; Blackie; Darkie;
Liamin; Butcher; Gunnier;
Martie; Mucker;
Each one now a memory
Of monstrous proportion.
School, that hell hole of creation

Supplied early friends;
And slobberers:
Mullaney; English; Gildea;
Gannon; Llewellyn; Quinn;
Regan; Melvin; Grimes;
Conway; Dowd; Mangan.
A youth unlimited.
A borrowed bike could
Reach the vicissitudes of Bunniconlon;
the seedy sights and sounds of Easkey;
The extra-ordinariness of Ballina.
It provided trains;
Trains to remove the removables
To further fields of filth and fun.
But a heart sometimes yearns for return;
Return to where it started thumping;
Started a lifelong habit of a beat.
So I again look outward from that pier.
Fewer boats await;
Newer faces abate;
Remaining ones cheer.
I love you Enniscrone,
Inis Eascraic Abhann,
Isle of the Fishy River.
Your changing face
Changes not my feelings.

Triple By-Pass

Three men, one seat: one looking into a paper, one looking into his mobile; and one looking into his heart.

There was a little distance between each one. As I flew by on a bus, I tried to imagine what each one was thinking.

A (Adam?) was reading the Daily Mail - his usual daily. Wasn't one of those sick Irishmen who indulged in the Irish Times every day; or that shit paper the Indo. Liked a good read, did Adam. Liked to read of his favourite football team, see. That and the page three's - bleedin' Irish birds didn't look like tha'. Massive. Anyway…Liverpool had a good win, thanksbetojayus. No way they'll not be in Europe next season now. They'll put them ponsie United in their place. Yeah.

B (Brixie?) was sending an e-mail to his bird. Wanting to meet her later. Suggested she bring a few quid. He'd just put on a bet and lost. Poxy. He hated losing, especially to friggin' bookies. He'd worked hard for that. Must have taken an hour to talk his ould fella into partin' with it. Still, didn't like to be always asking her for some dosh either. Didn't seem right. But he had this interview on Friday. Should get it. Even then it'd be weeks before he'd any decent money in his pocket. Jeez… will ya answer me, woman? I could mill a pint right now.

C (Cadooka?)- was having a bad day. Since he arrived in Ireland he'd become accustomed to such. Each day had a sameness. Like at home, maybe. Except he wasn't being harassed here. He could do what he liked. Except he liked to work, and couldn't. Had been told in a restaurant he could work but only for three euro hour, and for fifty-five hours. He was desperate … .but not stupid. Didn't like the way the 'nice' Irish treated him and his like. Wasn't fair.

"Now … here I am on a seat, in North Strand. Two others share. They don't care. A bus flying by. Bloke upstairs looking down. Caught my eye. Seems old. Old and grey. Wonder what he does? Does he travel on buses looking at people? Does he try to imagine what they are thinking? Don't wonder about me, Irishman. You don't know what I am thinking. Still, I wish we could share thoughts. Wonder if he's a writer?"

Surviving the Forties

There was little in the way of 'facilities' in villages, then.

No great roads, for one thing. The best of them resembled a 'bohreen', with a skelp of tar thrown on it. They tended to be high in the middle, sloping down at both sides. To get around on a bike was always a problem - if you had a bike that is?

We had one, but much later. It wasn't 'ours' as such though - it was my sister's. To get a use of it was seen as a big deal. I saw my mother trying to master the intricacies of the vehicle a few times, and she was having problems with it, I think; certainly staying straight wasn't something that came easy. That would have been around 1950. Her first time on a bike, ever, she said.

With us, though, the horse, and the pony were our real modes of transport. What a wonderfully versatile animal is the horse. Before Mr. Ford came along with his tractor, or was it Mr. Ferguson? The horse did all the farm work. For us alone, two fine heavy animals were so important. Now, of course, you only see them running and jumping, and earning good money for their owners.

Being born into a way of life means that it is taken as 'normal'. You carry on, and do it without thinking. Nowadays, it is often said that such carry-on was nothing but slavery. Maybe it is the spoiled brats of today, who have some gadget or other to do everything for them, that say this. I didn't think so, to be honest.

The older members of the family surely worked harder than I did, and for many more years, too; so maybe the gradual change was already under way? We may all talk of it all now as almost romantic - but there and then, there was little romance to it, I can tell you.

The 'townies', of course, thought that the likes of me had a great time. 'Privileged' is the word I heard one of them use, if you don't mind. Sure maybe they were right. It's not everyone has the opportunity to spend up to eighty hours a week at work for no pay. What did the poor under-privileged little divils have to do? Maybe an hour, running for messages to the shop, for instance. Maybe for a lump of tobacco for the ould fella; or twenty Players; or a lump of soap, and a brown loaf for the mother. Tough going, surely?

There's the point of the farming family having relatively little to buy in the shops, seeing as how they would be growing most of their needs in the fields, or in the farm-yard. True. But my goodness, it was hard work; beasts don't rear themselves, and neither do chickens. Corn doesn't grow without a lot of loving care; indeed, neither does grass. Cows don't stand over a bucket twice a day, and 'let go' with the milk. Privileged? Sure.

But, a village then, even, had to have its own survival tricks. The men-folk, mostly, had to put in the forty, or more likely fifty, hours to earn the crust. It might be running a wee shop; or working in a bank, probably in the nearest town; or teaching in the local school.

Or indeed, putting in the hours of hardship on some foreign soil. That surely accounted for a helluva lot of folk in those stringent times. Even more so in the Fifties. I saw whole rows of houses being emptied of grown men. Followed by the family, when he had the makings of a living secured; maybe in Birmingham, or Camden, or Boston.

What sickening, heart-breaking decisions had to be made by so many. What sad facts remained at the heart of those decisions: their own country couldn't supply a living for its citizens. Citizens who had grown with the new country, and endured all its pain and passion. Those left at home had to carry-on, of course.

The life of a small community, then as now rotates often on an axis of support. It is inter-dependant. And the farmer was an intricate part of this support. The Fair Day, for instance, not only brought the opportunity for some to add to their herd, and for others to sell off those ready for sale, and bring in that all-important shilling or two. It also brought much needed relief for the shopkeeper, and the bar owner. The morning's work would have to be rewarded with liquid of some sort; and the wife would have her own list of priorities. The shawl and apron would be discarded, and the best coat donned for this special occasion - shopping day. Many's the word of gossip would be swapped, indeed, and acquaintances renewed, during those all-important meetings.

Meanwhile, 'the boss' would be feeling just a bit pleased with himself, as the bottles of stout, or whiskey, would be emptied slowly. Not that any word of such a feeling would ever be uttered. Not likely. It is not in the nature of the farmer to indulge in such nonsense. Instead, it must be made plain to all listening how hard and cruel the life is they are living; and how they would not be at it at all if there was any chance of any alternative work.

When, and if, the wife deigned to join him later, it would have to be in the 'snug' of course, those nice hidden-away little secluded corners, where she couldn't easily be spotted 'letting the side down'.

Some pubs had a grocery counter as well, maybe taking up one side. This was probably to give potential customers more than one reason to visit. Mind you, it also pointed out the delicate understanding by the wily publican of the nature of some of his occasional visitors. For instance, if a house-keeper happened to drop in for that loaf of bread, or pound of butter, it was a sure bet that the eyes would wander to the other side of the premises just before leaving. Then, as if on a whim, the shoes would take her in that direction, and the small demi, or the half naggin, or the wee bottle of gin would join it's more sober friends at the bottom of the shopping bag.

There is no doubt but there existed a fair bit of snobbery then. A sort of 'class division', in a way. Clearly defined, and strangely accepted. By most, anyway. There would inevitably be a golf club. Probably small, and 'select'. Probably, also, comprised of people who indulged in the delusion of being 'a sportsman'. It is my contention that a very small percentage, indeed, of those could actually play the game, to any degree of proficiency. But play they would. Religiously every Sunday morning, and possibly on Thursdays, too. Perhaps the reward lay in the 'lounge', though? Here, when the plus fours, and the mashie, and the niblick were so carefully stored away, our hero's could have a treat or two, - perhaps from the bottle rather than the tap? And talk of the day's wonderful achievements on the fairways and greens. One was, after all, talking to equals now.

What a strange and weird creation we are, really. Anyway, all this is only to give an inkling of the varied and, betimes desolate life of folk in those decades.

But, this country boy had plans. Fair enough, I wasn't the brightest on the planet; or even in my own limited little world. The times weren't exactly brimming with hope and promise, either. But hey, a boy can dream, right? Boy did I dream. I may have been sharing a sagging bed with a brother or two; may have been starved of any show of emotion, even though I wouldn't have recognised it if came up and hugged me; may even have accepted the world around me as the best possible. But, as I say, I had plans.

I think they started with my dreams. Some of them were 'real'. I mean the kind that happen to ya when sound asleep, and then the mind goes walk-about - taking you to places of wonder; or of fright. Others used happen when I'd take myself away from the work, and the study. Where would I go? Easy - just across the road and into the sand-hills.

Sometimes, I'd go with my sister, Chris. She was cool. At least, now she's 'cool' - then she was probably 'alright.' To sit on the hills over-looking the road about 200 yards away, meant we could survey the passing scene, and comment on it, even, without being part of it. We could see our house, too. It was there, but it was at least for the moment, 'somewhere else'.

Then, our talk would be of London, and Leicester Square, and Piccadilly Circus, and the 'Tubes'. I loved all that. It was an escape into a world I could barely imagine, to be honest.

Then, when I was up there on my own, I would let the imagination run free. So what were my big dreams? And plans.? Maybe it was Radio Luxemburg, or such, that had my poor ould head addled, but I tell you this - I was gonna be a star. Movie star? Yer never know. I was no Burt bleedin' Lancaster, and I knew it. Norman Wisdom maybe. But that was hardly an aspiration, more a fear. No, I was going to be a singing star. Yeah. Me. But that was the time of Bing Crosby and Ann Shelton and such.? Okay, good point, but there was better, too.

I had listened to the likes of Hank Williams and thought he was mighty. This cowboy singing, with a story in the song - I was impressed with the idea. I'd do that I said. I used to practice, but only when no-one was listening. Once I sent away for the words and music, to a Dublin store, of a few songs, and I learned them off by heart.

So, my dreams were taking shape. Sing in front of a band, I thought. They'd all clap, and say I was brilliant. Did it happen? Naw.. well, it did, sort of, but not for another twenty years.

But it was my first aspiration, in a time when such things were in short supply. My friend Christy used say he'd be a film star, alright. I think it was Gary Cooper that he was gonna be. He'd sometimes talk like him, right enough; and draw the imaginary gun, etc. I don't know though. Sure he was only little, like. I mentioned Alan Ladd, but I don't think he was impressed. I think it was a thing we did then - dream. Maybe an unconscious wish to escape the lives we had? Maybe.?

Or maybe it was the tales told by those that would return from those far exotic places - New York or Liverpool? We'd only hear them second or third hand of course, and maybe the contents would have slightly changed, but it surely got our imaginations going.

Anyone for a laugh? Places of entertainment were not part of the deal, in the forties. Indeed, to be seen enjoying yourself at all would probably be looked on with suspicion. But, there were official times for levity. Sunday night was one, and the local dance-hall was the venue. This was something to be approached with a certain amount of seriousness, though. Preparation could take a lot of time; shoes polished to a perfect shine, the crease in the trousers had to be straight and obvious; the hair washed, combed and quiffed. The ladies would take even longer. Then finally, the serious business of dancing would be engaged in. Knowing the steps for every intricate number was a prerequisite. Being unable to dance more than adequately was like consigning yourself to the dustbin of the forgotten. 'Starting off on the wrong foot' would be too kind a way to express that first impression on the lady of your choice.

The bould Mick Del and those innumerable other big bands of the time, with their brass and wind, had a precipitation that would equal any in the world at the time, I'd say. Indeed, some dance-halls, or ballrooms as they preferred to be called, were favoured over others, if the floor was of a certain quality - maybe parquet or some such, and would thereby attract big bands from overseas as well. Though I have no clear memory of Mr. Ellington or Mr. Basie ever blessing us with their presence.

To be honest, though, I couldn't understand how the women used be so interested in some of those lads, then. While we, as kids could see on film, the likes of Mr. Grant or Tracy being so sophisticated and charming, and all that stuff. Then we'd see the local equivalent trying it on, and to be honest, it would be nothin' but embarrassing.

You see, my aunt owned the dance-hall, then, and she would sometimes get me to help take in the coats, or assist with the teas, etc. While it wasn't my favourite past-time, it did have advantages. I could see and hear at first hand the carry-on of our heroes. To say I learned how not to treat or talk to women was probably my best lesson. Oh now. Still, I suppose some of the women weren't too pushed.

There was also the cinema. I believe it was Friday nights that this particular den of pernickety opened its doors to entertain the populace. Sure Christy and I used get thrown out sometimes, with other undesirables, for maybe pushing people off the long forms that we'd be put on, right in front of the screen. We'd often manage to creep in again; back door or window.

It used surprise me how the adults would get so caught up in the films, though. All the way home you'd hear them discussing the ins and outs of the plot; and how they maybe didn't agree with the ending; or how 'yer wan's hair was nothing less than a disgrace.' Strange people, adults, we all decided.

Probably it was the 'Serials' that we enjoyed most. 'Don Winslow' was one. He was a real hot-shot. Do you know that once, when surrounded in a house, by at least a hundred baddies, he took out his machine-gun and shot every last one of them. Yerr a, hero? That's the kind ya want, like The Reality of 'Innocence.'

To describe that decade in a few words is difficult. You'd think not, that the obvious words would cover the thing adequately. But I don't think so. Drab ? Yes. Innocent? to a degree, perhaps. But also, no.

There was a certain 'knowing-ness' that said: 'We are too aware of the realities of our world; and they are not nice. We are consigned to live in this time, and we soldier manfully on, dealing with the world as we find it. We will make progress and hand on a world more fair and more bearable to the next generation.

So 'innocence' doesn't seem to me to be the essence of such a reality. What is? I know not the word. But I do know that the people of 'then' suffered enormously from the aftermath of what went before. The wonderful heart and will of the Irish people ensured that they came out of it, with a positiveness and determination that is to be hugely admired.

Winging Ways

Soaring skywards into
the doughty wind
they fly. Eyes keen,
spotting from on high.

The occasional morsel
from finicky human hand.
Re-action is swift, as
competition may lurk.

Replenished, they
rise again. Using the
helpful wind now,
unfettered by time.

Peace

I long for a time of nothingness;
A time when the clock stands still.
Only then will I sit, and listen to
The dust settling on the windowsill.

Listen to the movement of the wind
Sidling through the chimney pots;
Sometimes noisy, sometimes quiet,
But always there, and reassuring.

I will smile at the unimportance of it all.
Shake my head at the years of turmoil,
When every second had to be accounted for,
And each day a monument to the cause.

This time will temper my soul;
Trample on my worrying nature;
Rest my too long aching heart;
And lay bare the beauty of being.

An Appreciation

Doctor dimmed the blinding lights. Patients faced the night-time hours with hopeful expectations. Six lives released into the medical care of people dedicated totally to their welfare. Thoughts, talks, mumblings, grumblings, moans, cries, laughter - all slowly crumble to a relative silence; and the night hours tick their way towards a distant but waiting dawn.

Night staff relax not. Though the scurry of a daytime ward diminishes in intensity, their little darlings still must be watched, listened to, tended to, cajoled into a quietude. Taking of pressures, temperatures, and administering of doses, at designated hours, continues without fuss. Also, staff communication gains a certain momentum about now. Cosy teas bring forth the stories, comments, worries, jokes in the busy lives of a modern youth.

I smile before sleep, knowing that patience, and obedience are all I have to contribute on my road to wellsville.

Down Time

There were a lot of things bothering Doyle as he walked the beach. Maybe it was the aftermath of Christmas, and all its hullabaloo that was the cause of it? He surely was glad it was over, anyway.

Being single, he always felt a little left out. Oh he was popular alright about then. Family kept welcoming him, and making a fuss. Their children even more so; he could see the expectation in their eyes as he would arrive. 'What did he bring me?' - the big question. Sometimes he thought that if he was a father himself, the whole bloody thing would cost less.

He'd even developed a great dislike for wine - he that could put it away no problem, when younger. Now, the customary bottle had to be brought here and there, and the customary: 'ya shouldn't have,' accompanied by the almost concealed 'not another bloody bottle of wine. Couldn't he have been more adventurous?' Aye, maybe he could, but he could also have stayed away and saved himself the torture of repetitiveness.

Maybe he was being cantankerous; 'but sure we're a funny ould creation,' he thought then. For weeks before the bloody thing, wasn't he looking forward to it as much as the next. Caught up in the celebration, I suppose. More bloody drink put away than was smart, and more money spent than was sensible. Maybe the break from work was the spur? No doubt of that.

And maybe Deirdre being off as well? Maybe. But sure she was missing for more time than she was available. The mammy wasn't likely to want her spending her precious time with the likes of him, when she could be useful at home. Yerra, ould ones can be fierce selfish too.

Fair enough - they talked plenty on phones, but sure ya can't put yer hands on her through a blasted phone line.

Doyle sat down on a rock, and contemplated. Two more days off. What the hell would he do with them? Herself wouldn't be back until the following night, which shortened his options. Could go into town; maybe look at some of the sales? Sales, is it? Sales me arse. With everything ending in 99 cent, and most of it unneeded. Sure the people in business must take the public to be shockin' stupid entirely. No more shoppin' for him, and that's for sure.

What then? Go down and see that gang of crackpots, and start all over again? Sure that'd be like normality. Too soon, dammit.

He looked at the sea, going in and out, and not givin' a friggin damn what he did - or what the whole world did either. Maybe that was the answer? Be cool. Be confident. Be positive. He walked again. The gaggle of sea birds around somehow cheered him up. Other people walking seemed happy, somehow, with their own gaggle.

His phone rang. It was his mother. Their conversation seemed strange, almost. No giving out, no recriminations, just wishing him a sincere good New Year. Funny how the right words can have a right affect. Then it rang again. 'God blasht ya,' he shouted, knowing that the next one would bring the wrong words entirely. Is there no bloody escape from this damn thing?'

He wasn't going to answer it. But it kept ringing. Hello. 'he shouted, then.

'That's a nice welcome, I must say,' said Deirdre. 'Deirdre.

'Jaysus is it yerself? Howya?'

'Just ringing to say a proper hello, Doyle. And to tell you I love you.' Then she hung up.

Doyle smiled. 'Maybe th'ould world ishn't that bad, begod, after all?'

Footie

They share a city,
Share a game.
They share a passion,
But are ne'er the same.

Blues or Reds take your pick,
Toffee or Tout; Scouser or Mick.
Games the same, goals so wide
Ninety minutes nowhere to hide

In hearts there is an enmity
A town divided there to see.
If A beats B, or B beats A
There'll be more than a mere hurray!

And still there is a sporting gear
That clicks in August every year.
Let me now say as I keep my cool:
God Bless 'All in Liverpool'.

Quay Cargo

Bonking bunkers
in silhouette defy
the eyes avoidance as I
traverse lonely quays.

Liffey waters lap the
green dirt walls, inviting
investigation towards
its pastoral source.

Shop windows beckon,
enthral and educate,
with their variegated ware;
serving the wily public.

People pass, pause, rush,
hurry. All the time in earnest
chatter; communicating their
diverse commonality.

Nuffsaid

Oh, take me away from
this ordered world
of tidiness, and weed-less
gardens of forgetfulness.

Remove my ageing body
and drop it on a hillside
festooned with dappled
Hopkins' and you.

Odyssey

How to sum up India, and my experiences there?

Maybe I need to be absent from it all for some time to give an accurate description. It is still too much in my mind, perhaps; too much in my soul. But, an initial verdict should, at least, be possible.

When deciding to go, I felt I was doing it for me, as much as for my sister who has spent most of her life there. I'd been very much stuck in a rut, in a way. Each day had taken on a sameness. A reluctance to move had inserted itself in my psyche, and soon I was confined to a reclining circle. I'd always had a lack of appreciation of the 'accepted' circle of destinations that seem to somehow satisfy the otherwise wise.

To go to the eternal troubles of preparation for travel, with its inserted waiting, queuing, paying, waiting, and trying to eat 'food' out of a minute plastic dish, without room to stretch elbows, even; then go through the waiting again, etc. and all this so we can have the enormous benefit of being able to lie, with endless others, probably British, on a ropey beach for a few weeks. This smells of a deterioration of brain in the smiling tourist, to my mind.

So..the reluctant tourist? In shovels. Then, India entered the equation. Different, I thought. I'd always had a fascination with countries such as Russia, China and India. Also parts of South America. Places where I'd at least have an opportunity to broaden my diminishing mind. New experiences not variations on familiars. The fact that my eldest sister was most unlikely to come home again, was a deciding factor. She's a missionary, and has been there most of her life; also a nurse. The fact that my gorgeous niece had made the offer, made the decision easier too. We'd always got on well. Plus she'd been in India a few times before.

Then there was up to two months to go before leaving. That time had its share of doubt. Between the talking, resisting, listening, almost shirking, and considering all that was said to me about the place, it was at times doubtful that I'd ever get there at all. The advice came from all quarters - don't drink the water; don't eat the food ... unless it's well cooked, boiled or fried; don't ever attempt to drive on the roads; don't try to cross the roads. And the people? They're everywhere - all the time. And the heat? - at least 100 degrees. And the flies?

Then the references to my age, my poor health, my ability to cope. Not exactly encouraging. But we were going anyway. The journey from Heathrow to Bangalore took just ten hours. For me, this was a frightening thought, but it somehow passed quite easily. A pre-paid taxi and we were there.

That taxi ride gave me inklings of what was to come, and what to expect. The crowds; the apparent poverty; the bad-bad-roads; the noisy traffic; continual beeping of horns; the ramshackle state of most houses, at least around where I was going to stay. The absence of white bodies suggested we'd get more attention - even my sister looks Indian now.

But any worries were soon dispersed. Where we stayed, with her, was a little haven. They had sunk their own well, so water wasn't a problem. Their garden was a refuge, and one of the most peaceful places I ever stayed in. The care and fuss inherent in all the inhabitants was lavished on us, and how good it was to feel so welcome. I couldn't wait to go walkabout, and this I, we did plenty of.

At first glance, the place sure looked a mess. But I soon came to realise that it wasn't necessarily so. Each hovel seemed to contain a business; everyone seemed to have their own little deal going on; in other words - things worked.

The roads and footpaths were in continual upheaval, and in fact most seemed to walk on the roads, out of necessity. Fine, except for the plethora of rickshaws, taxis, buses, lorries, bikes, motorbikes - all occupying the same road. The great mystery is how there aren't many more accidents every day - I never saw even one collision.

Very soon, I found, you adjust to the situation. This is how it is, you can't do anything about it; so enjoy it. We did. The people were very friendly. 'What country?' they ask. 'You are most welcome.' Sure you get stares - her more than me. But so what? Sure you get a degree of begging. But neither, we found, were really intrusive. If one were to get so, then you manage to get it into their head that perhaps a cessation of such might be in their best interest.

The children were a revelation. Really beautiful, with that perfect brown skin, white teeth, and eternal smiles. And how they wanted to chat.

Animals seem to play a big part in the day to day. The cows, strangely, are not so much wandering around in droves, as by the side of the side roads, and kept for their milk. 'Tending the herd' here does have a slightly different meaning.

A lot of dogs, but not a problem, except when they decide to join in the midnight chorus. I didn't get a rabies injection, and didn't need it.

In some places, a lot of monkeys, or maybe mongoose. Saw a few wild elephant, and lions. Couldn't wait to get into the countryside, though.

So we travelled. Trains, like the buses not in the best of repair, but they worked. Like the buses, very cheap. Kerala was worth the journey. So different. A large state, that seems more rich and prosperous than other places we'd seen. Maybe the climate is the reason. We saw only two real rainfalls, both at night, and both thunderous.

Now we were in the regions of tea plantations, plus coffee plantations. They just seem to go on for many miles. The smell from the flowering coffee trees was filling the air, and really pungent. The reams of women working in the tea farms, with bags and what-nots to protect them from the sun, and insects. Then the 'tidier' paddy-fields. So neat and so efficient looking. Again, people working in them all hours. Some better houses to be seen here too, but not owned by the workers, one suspects. There's talk of some 'lords' still in ownership.

A bus over and through a mountain range was a particular memory. We climbed one. The scenes and valleys beneath the best I ever seen. But generally, away from all that, you see little variation from the palm trees. Dry season means little grass between. I'd need to go North, I suspect, to find more variation on this theme, but not on this journey. We stayed in four different locations, and the hotels were just fine. Food varied enough to suit all tastes. Beer available, but limited. Though the Kingfisher Strong was certainly that.

Stayed very close to the Arabian Sea - in fact practically over it. Impressive.

Our journey back to Bangalore took seven hours, overnight. Quid an hour. Generally, the heat varied between 28 and 34 degrees; but I found it most acceptable. Nice breeze. Did get severe burns on my feet and legs, but that was my own fault, and all part of the deal. Aloe vera helped.

Overall? Very good indeed. Very tiring, I admit, but schedules could have been planned better. Suffered no health problems whatsoever, and only normal precautions necessary.

Peculiarities? Hard to get used to everyone eating with their right hand, and mixing up the food, etc. It's not recorded what the left hand is used for, though I did notice that toilet paper is not provided. Seem consumed by religion. Churches, mosques, temples everywhere (visited a few). Went to an Indian Mass - very impressive. Invited to a concert too, but maybe I was slightly too old to feel appreciation. Very Indian, and how the kids loved it.

Return journey okay.; but 19 hours in total. Will I go again? Maybe, in about four years. To go Varanasi way would be a new experience again, I believe. But then, Russia beckons too. Now home one week, and just got energy back.

Progress

Restrictions in my life
keep me tethered.
My 'to-hell-with-it' nature
needs some curtailing.

In my youth, that other
world, my whole life
was a restriction.
I grew up enchained.

'Do this; be quiet; who asked
you? Stand up; sit down;
say your prayers; say you're
sorry; speak up; shut up.'

Now, as an ageing father, when
independence should be welcoming
me into the fold, I find I'm still
playing the game; and losing.

So, the potential rake within
is imprisoned, and slowly dies.
Those that survive and prosper
have my full admiration.

Facing It

I saw her face yesterday.
Though knowing her, I was shocked.
That face that once had won my heart
now looked so lined, so drawn, so … wan.

I recalled when and where
I first saw that face.
When I first kissed that smile,
and gazed into her loving eyes.

I recalled the hours spent together;
endless, beautiful, love-filled hours.
We were inseparable; 'well-suited', they said.
Yet, here we were, strangers.

How life throws us around in circles.
How to survive the exigencies -
and our mistakes - as we trundle along,
is something we struggle to learn.

Silences

I must be talking to myself,
such is the response.
I want to shout my head off;
I know I need to - just once.

I must go talk to the table,
tell it that I'm not pleased.
Enumerate the changes,
the problems I want teased.

Maybe if I shout at the dog,
really get it off my chest;
He might agree it's good to talk,
then we both can rest.

I hate not being able
to express myself at all.
If I didn't think so much
that might solve it all?

Sometimes I see the dipsticks
being asked about the world;
But no-one ever asks me
if I would like a twirl?

I represent 'the ordinary'
and no-one ever asks,
If I think my representatives
a genius, or an ass?

No, they don't care what I think,
those people of great note;
But I guess I'll have the final word
when exercising my vote.

Solitude

Sitting quiet, feeling blue,
with coffee cold, and thoughts of you.
Not a sound in house to hear;
then distant barking rents the air.

Sometimes I longed for silent days,
away from worldly noise and care.
Now, imagined bliss put to the test;
but troubled mind can know no rest.

Yes, troubled mind and troubled soul;
results no doubt, of life's own goals.
Few can travel this worldly trail
without the need of lengthy bail.

But now my mind is occupied
with thoughts of you, and all we hide.
We hurt and scorn, and all the while
our love sees not a single smile.

Why do we always seem to try
to preserve a foolish pride?
When all our hearts really desire
is honesty, and end of ire.

And so, as life intrudes again,
I promise to find strength within
To say: 'I 'm sorry. I love you,
and hope we can both start anew.'

Feelings

Is loneliness a coat you wear
Is there a silent cry that rents the air
Do you reach for him when there's no-one there
Or do you enjoy being 'Miss Solitaire'

Have you longed to be what you once called free
Or is your independence a 'fait accompli'
Are you free of the need to need someone
Can you stand up and say: Just me alone

In the long small hours do you long for love
Have you sacrificed feelings for push and shove
Or somewhere inside, do embers burn
Would it be good to love, and be loved in return?

Symbols

Red; dark-red tresses
caress your slender neck.
Cascading curls enhance
your tempting lips.

Red warning signs are flashing
as I reach out to touch.
But you are out of reach,
and I am out of time.

Meanwhile

Let mirth and death go hand in hand
encourage not this sleight of hand.
Where fear and tear doth colour blue
the coming from and going to.

We're going to, with strut and style
with every stab and every smile.
Each suffered pain, each strident joy
each coming from each girl and boy.

Some of us baulk at hurdles high;
priorities stilly put by.
Some are more certain of the game
and recognise the rules and shame.

On journeys end it's true to say
I'll ask for nought but huge fair play.
But please, my friend, say 'tisn't so
That someone, somewhere will say: I KNOW.

A Writer's Lament

As I finished my meanderings
I realised too late - too true
I'd left an ice cream melting
As I eat it up - I wished 'twas you!